SYNTHETIC POLYMERS

FRED W. BILLMEYER, JR. began his study of polymers as a graduate student at Cornell University, under the direction of Nobel Prize winner Peter Debye. After earning his doctorate at Cornell in 1945, Dr. Billmeyer spent several years of active polymer research in the plastics industry and as Lecturer in High Polymers at the University of Delaware. During this period he also served for one year as Visiting Professor in Chemical Engineering at the Massachusetts Institute of Technology.

Since 1964 Dr. Billmeyer has held the position of Professor of Analytical Chemistry at Rensselaer Polytechnic Institute, where his duties include teaching and research in both polymer science and the science of color measurement. He is the author of over 125 technical papers in the fields of polymer chemistry and optics and, in addition, has written three textbooks on polymers as well as *Principles of Color Technology* (with Max Saltzman).

Dr. Billmeyer has traveled widely in the United States and Europe, lecturing, attending technical meetings, and vacationing with his family. His major hobby for the past few years has been installing a cathedral-size pipe organ in his home. Dr. Billmeyer lives with his wife Annette and three teen-age children in Niskayuna, New York.

Synthetic Polymers

BUILDING THE GIANT MOLECULE

FRED W. BILLMEYER, JR.

Doubleday & Company, Inc., Garden City, New York
1972

Library of Congress Catalog Card Number 77–171279
Copyright © 1972 by Doubleday & Company, Inc.
All Rights Reserved
Printed in the United States of America
First Edition

THE SCIENCE STUDY SERIES

The Science Study Series offers to students and to the general public the writings of distinguished authors on the most stirring and fundamental topics of science, from the smallest known particles to the whole universe. Some of the books tell of the role of science in the world of man, his technology, and civilization. Others are biographical in nature, telling the fascinating stories of the great discoverers and their discoveries. All the authors have been selected both for expertness in the fields they discuss and for ability to communicate their special knowledge and their own views in an interesting way. The primary purpose of these books is to provide a survey within the grasp of the young student or the layman. Many of the books, it is hoped, will encourage the reader to make his own investigations of natural phenomena.

The Series, which now offers topics in all the sciences and their applications, had its beginning in a project to revise the secondary schools' physics curricula. At the Massachusetts Institute of Technology, during 1956, a group of physicists, high school teachers, journalists, apparatus designers, film producers, and other specialists organized the Physical Science Study Committee, now operating as part of Educational Development Center, Newton, Massachusetts. They pooled their knowledge and experience toward the design and creation of aids to the learning of physics. Initially, their effort was supported by the National Science Foundation, which has continued to aid the program. The Ford Foundation, the Fund for the Advancement of Education, and the Alfred P. Sloan Foundation have also given support. The Committee has created a textbook, an extensive film series, a laboratory guide, especially designed apparatus, and a teachers' source book.

CONTENTS

PART II

CHARACTERIZING POLYMER MOLECULES

PART III

POLYMER PROPERTIES
AND MOLECULAR STRUCTURE

PART I

The Molecular Nature
of Synthetic Polymers

Chapter 1

WHAT ARE GIANT MOLECULES?

Have you ever thought about what it would be like to
grow very, very small—to shrink, like Alice in Wonderland but still more, until even the things we can see only
under a microscope are much larger than we? If we could
become, say, a hundred million times smaller than our
present size—but somehow retain our own form and
senses—what would we see around us?

We can only guess, of course, but possibly we would
find that everything around us looked like rather fuzzy
marbles of various sizes, some of them stuck together
in groups of two or more. We might find ourselves stand-
ing on a somewhat mushy surface of this sort of material,
and see many pairs of the fuzzy balls floating around in
space nearby, colliding with one another frequently.

These objects are what we call *molecules,* by which we
mean, without attempting to get a precise definition,
groups of atoms sufficiently firmly stuck—bonded, more
properly—together to exist independent of their neighbors
and to hold together under a variety of circumstances.

Most of the molecules with which we are familiar contain only a few atoms. Those double ones floating around,
for example, are the oxygen and nitrogen making up the
air we breathe. The chemists designate them by the shorthand formulas O_2 and N_2. Water, H_2O, has three atoms:
one oxygen and two hydrogen. Propane, the "bottled gas"
used for a cooking fuel in many rural areas, has a few
more: its formula is C_3H_8, where the letter C, of course,
represents an atom of carbon.

But look, there is a long molecule lying near our feet

that resembles a piece of rope, or a very long chain of beads. Let's walk alongside it and see how long it is. It extends for quite a way, perhaps a hundred feet compared to our size, or more. This is really a giant molecule compared to the others we have seen.

Scientists have discovered in the last thirty years or so that a great many molecules are made up of very large numbers of atoms, thousands upon thousands of them, truly deserving to be called giants in comparison to their more common neighbors. We call these giants *polymers,* a word meaning "made up of many parts."

Now this literal definition of the word polymer is not very helpful, and the major purpose of this book is to develop a picture of the structure of polymer molecules, paying special attention to those features of their structure that make these giant molecules useful to man. Before explaining their nature, let us explore these uses a bit more.

WHAT ARE POLYMERS USED FOR?

Now that we have at least a vague idea of what the giant molecules of polymers are like, it is logical to ask what, if any, value they have for our lives. What good are these long, wriggly molecules?

The answer to this last question comes through loud and clear: We are *made* of polymers, and without them no life of any kind as we know it could exist. All protein material, including the very muscles and sinews of our bodies, as well as much of the food we eat, is composed of polymer molecules, which are in fact much more complex than the ones we will describe in this book. Even our intelligence depends on the existence of very special polymer molecules forming the genes and chromosomes that determine our heredity.

After this, it may seem like an anticlimax to say that the long-chain nature of polymers is essential to two other groups of materials that are a common and vital part of our lives. The first of these is *fibers,* a major constituent of all vegetable matter, including cotton and cellulose, and the second is *elastomers.* Without polymers, there would be no such thing as rubber, and only a very few fibrous materials.

All of the polymers mentioned so far occur in nature; nothing has yet been said about synthetic polymers, the particular subject of this book. What do they do for us? One answer that impresses me and my colleagues, but which you may want to challenge, is that many of the most exciting and important scientific and engineering advances of this age could not exist without man-made polymers. Let me give you just a few examples.

Take the automobile. Where would it be, as a part of our modern society, without rubber? It is true that automobile tires were once made entirely of natural, rather than synthetic, rubber, but today the tire industry, by far the largest consumer of both natural and synthetic rubbers, uses over twice as much synthetic rubber as the natural product. In addition to this major dependence on rubber, your car could not have an automatic transmission without synthetic polymers for seals and gaskets, could not have hydraulic brakes or power steering without synthetic polymers for hoses and cables, and could not have a modern ignition system without synthetic polymers as electrical insulators.

Consider television and radar. Without polyethylene, a synthetic polymer first made in 1936, for wire and cable insulators, these devices could not exist. The conquest of space is likewise dependent on man-made polymers. It takes over a ton of just one kind of synthetic polymer, polytetrafluoroethylene, to get a large rocket off the ground and its payload into orbit. Finally, think about your clothing. True, more cotton is still used than any other fiber for textiles, but what would your wardrobe be like today without nylon, the acrylics, or the wash-and-wear polyesters, all synthetic polymers?

WHEN DID MAN FIRST USE POLYMERS?

Of course, the ultimate answer to when man began to use polymers is as old as man himself, since from his very beginning man has depended on such naturally oc-

curring polymers as meat and vegetables for food; wood
and straw for shelter; leather, furs, and cotton and other
fibers for clothing; and, later, paper (cellulose) for com-
munication.

Many present-day uses of polymers had their origins
in ancient times. Five thousand years ago the Sumerians
and Babylonians used asphalt and pitch for floor covering
and paving (and it's a good bet that your basement recre-
ation room has an asphalt-tile floor today, and that you
traveled to school or work this morning over an asphalt-
containing macadam pavement). Naturally occurring
polymers were used by the ancient Egyptians to varnish
their sarcophagi, and varnish was, of course, used to pro-
tect wood and paintings in the Middle Ages. Shellac, the
polymeric secretion of the lac bug, came into use in the
1600s, but use of silk, likewise a polymeric secretion, this
one from the silkworm, predated this by many years.

What might be termed the modern use of polymers
began with the discovery in 1839 by Charles Goodyear
of how to convert rubber into a useful vulcanized form.
Rubber itself was introduced into Europe from South
America almost a hundred years earlier, and its name is
derived from its first real use, as an eraser. Other early
modifications of natural polymers into more useful forms
were the treatment of cellulose with acids to form cellulose nitrate and its conversion into celluloid in 1869 by
John Hyatt, and the production of acetate rayon fibers
and lacquers from cellulose acetate, first made in 1865
but not used extensively until the time of World War I.

The first commercial synthetic polymers were the
phenol-formaldehyde plastics made in 1907 by Leo
Baekeland and called "Bakelite." These materials are still
used in large quantities, amounting to about a billion
pounds a year. Since that time, of course, vast numbers
of synthetic polymers have been made, several on a similarly large scale. It is interesting that only a few of these
materials were the result of deliberate searches for new
materials having specifically desired properties, and several were discovered by pure accident.

One of the most widely popularized searches for a new

material was that of W. H. Carothers, which led to the discovery of nylon in 1939. But even here, Carothers and his co-workers were not primarily interested in the production of a new fiber, but in learning more about how to make polymers. Nylon was a fortunate by-product of their studies on the fundamentals of *polymerization,* the processes by which giant molecules are made. We will look further into this subject in Chapter 2.

Several polymers of great importance have been discovered by sheer accident. Polyethylene, familiar to you in a wide variety of uses ranging from baby bottles to film for packaging, is one of these. It was discovered in 1939 when certain chemicals were subjected to extremely high pressures in attempts to make other liquid molecules. The waxy solids that resulted from these experiments were entirely unexpected. Polytetrafluoroethylene was similarly discovered by accident some time later.

Polymer scientists like to think, however, that they now know enough about the structure of long-chain molecules to be able to "tailor" them to have desirable properties. This point can be debated, but there is no doubt that much has been learned about the nature of polymers in the last few decades.

WHEN WAS THE CHAIN NATURE
OF POLYMERS RECOGNIZED?

The mere fact that it is appropriate to ask when the long-chain nature of polymers was recognized suggests something unusual about the acceptance of this property of giant molecules, now considered an essential part of their nature. In fact, the great size of these molecules was recognized at least as long ago as 1861 by the Scottish chemist Thomas Graham, but it was sixty years later before it was widely accepted that polymer molecules are made up of long chains of atoms. Graham observed the sluggish behavior of some polymers when they are dissolved, and correctly attributed this to their large size. He invented the word *colloid,* meaning gluelike, to describe these substances. In time, it was recognized that such materials as rubber, cellulose, and starch belonged in this category.

But the term colloid was applied to a wide variety of substances, many of which, such as soap solutions, are not polymers in the sense we know them today. Materials of this sort consist of aggregates or groups of small molecules held together by strong intermolecular forces, but do not have the long-chain nature now associated with polymers. The aggregate structure was more readily accepted by the scientists of the late nineteenth century, who found it difficult to conceive of the existence of giant single molecules. Even after scientists learned how to make polymers and they became industrially important on a large scale, the aggregate idea persisted.

It was not, in fact, until Hermann Staudinger became convinced in the early 1920s of the long-chain nature of polymers that what we now accept as the correct interpretation of their structure began to be widely accepted. Staudinger was a remarkably versatile scientist, who investigated methodically both the synthesis and the properties of many polymers. He was persistent in his view that only long chains could account for his observations. His evidence was overwhelming and won for him the Nobel prize in 1953. In later chapters, we will review some of his findings and relate them to more modern ideas.

WHAT ARE POLYMERS LIKE?

If a polymer molecule is made up of many parts, many atoms, just how are these atoms arranged? Surely in a molecule containing, say, ten thousand atoms, there must be a guiding principle governing and explaining its structure. There is indeed, and not just one, but many. For the moment, let us concentrate on what is both the simplest and the most widespread—even universal—principle involved in polymers. As we saw in our imaginary visit to "atom land," their atoms are arranged in long chains consisting of many relatively simple groups strung together in a repeating pattern.

Let me use as an example a family of substances in which the repeating group of atoms consists of one carbon atom bonded to two hydrogens. We can write this repeating group as

$$\begin{array}{c} H \\ | \\ C \\ | \\ H \end{array}$$

or CH_2, where the lines indicate the bonds. This is not a complete molecule, but only a fragment. Chemists tell us that carbon atoms must form four bonds, so the atom of carbon we are concerned with must be bonded to two more atoms, in addition to the two we have indicated. If these also are hydrogens, we have

$$\begin{array}{c} H \\ | \\ H - C - H \\ | \\ H \end{array}$$

or $H - CH_2 - H$, which is the formula for the simplest complete molecule containing the CH_2 group. This is methane, which is the major constituent of natural gas.

I must point out here that the shorthand formulas I am using at this point to represent molecular structure are misleading in some respects. We cannot, for example, expect to represent the true three-dimensional nature of the methane molecule, which is illustrated in Figure 1 and Plate 1, by the two-dimensional formula I have used. For simplicity, however, I shall continue with formulas of the type $H - CH_2 - H$ as long as we have no need to consider these geometrical problems in detail.

It is a unique feature of the carbon atom that it can bond to itself as readily as to another atom. Thus, more complicated molecules in this hydrocarbon—that is, hydrogen plus carbon—family can be built up as follows: if two CH_2 groups are joined together, and each carbon makes its fourth bond to a hydrogen, we have $H - CH_2 - CH_2 - H$, which represents the gas ethane. Adding one more CH_2 group gives propane, $H - CH_2 - CH_2 - CH_2 - H$, whose formula we wrote

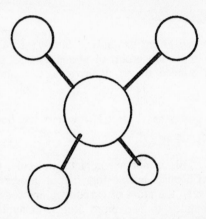

Fig. 1. A three-dimensional representation of the methane molecule, CH_4. Since we do not know what molecules really look like, we sometimes represent their atoms as balls, held together by sticks representing the bonds between them. These ball-and-stick models are usually adequate for describing the geometrical arrangement of the atoms, but do not show their space-filling properties correctly. This model shows that the four bonds of the carbon atom in methane are directed toward the four corners of a tetrahedron, each bond making the same angle of about 109.5° with each of the others.

previously as C_3H_8, a still more condensed way of describing the same molecule.

All these molecules, and some more complex ones such as butane, C_4H_{10}, are gases. But the next larger hydrocarbon, pentane, C_5H_{12}, is a liquid. Why? It is an experimental fact that everything in this universe tends to stick together a little bit. By this I mean that there are

Fig. 2. A few of the members of the paraffin family of chemical compounds. The long chain nature of these molecules is disguised by the shorthand method of writing their formulas. Instead of C_8H_{18}, a more realistic representation of octane

$$
\begin{array}{c}
\text{H} \quad \text{H} \quad \text{H} \quad \text{H} \quad \text{H} \quad \text{H} \quad \text{H} \quad \text{H} \\
| \quad\ | \quad\ | \quad\ | \quad\ | \quad\ | \quad\ | \quad\ | \\
\text{would} \qquad \text{be} \qquad \text{H} - \text{C} - \text{C} - \text{C} - \text{C} - \text{C} - \text{C} - \text{C} - \text{C} - \text{H.} \\
| \quad\ | \quad\ | \quad\ | \quad\ | \quad\ | \quad\ | \quad\ | \\
\text{H} \quad \text{H} \quad \text{H} \quad \text{H} \quad \text{H} \quad \text{H} \quad \text{H} \quad \text{H}
\end{array}
$$

Writing the formula for polyethylene in this way would take considerable time and space.

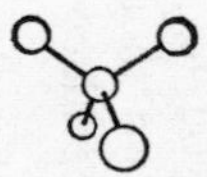

Methane
CH₄

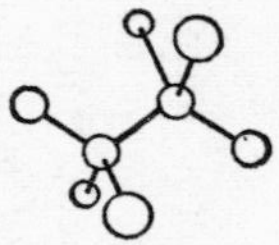

Ethane
C₂H₆

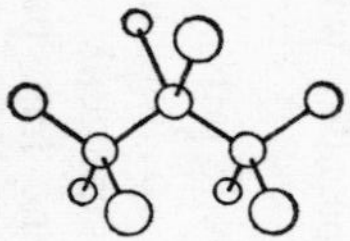

Propane
C₃H₈

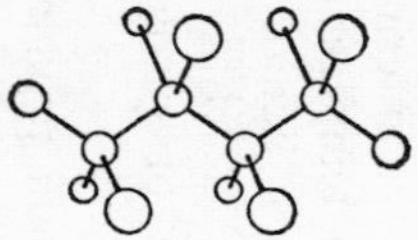

Butane
C₄H₁₀

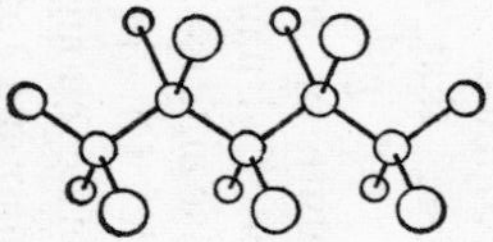

Pentane
C₅H₁₂

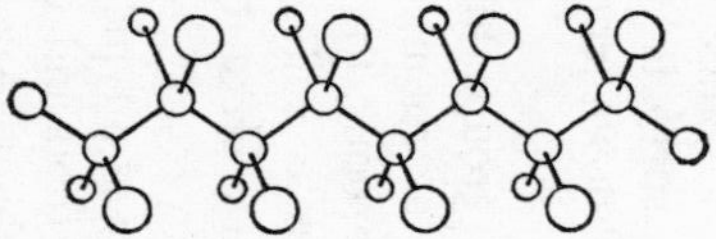

Octane
C₈H₁₈

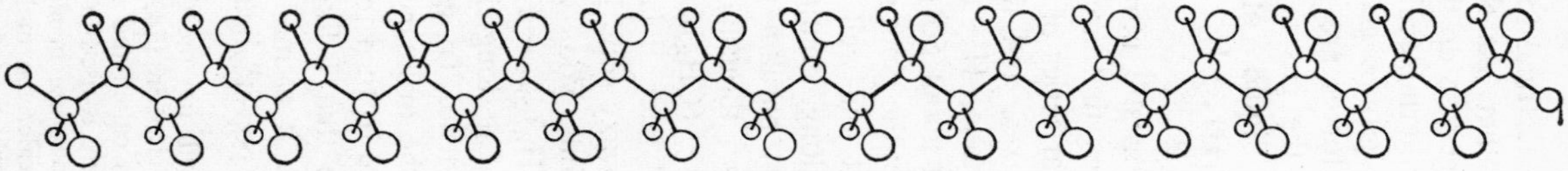

Triacontane
C₃₀H₆₂

always electrical forces tending to make molecules attract one another. As the number of atoms in the molecules gets larger, so do these forces of attraction between molecules (intermolecular forces, therefore). When the chain of CH_2 groups gets beyond four in length, the intermolecular forces are powerful enough at room temperature to pull the gas molecules together to form a liquid. A typical liquid of this sort is octane, C_8H_{18} or $H - (CH_2)_8 - H$, a well-known constituent of gasoline (Figure 2).

Adding still more CH_2 groups to the chain produces molecules that are solids at room temperature. In this particular series of hydrocarbons, these solids are the paraffin waxes, and the series is called the *paraffin* series. Triacontane, $H - (CH_2)_{30} - H$, a typical paraffin wax, melts at about 66°C.*

To get the giant molecule of a typical synthetic polymer, we must join well over a thousand CH_2 groups together in one long, continuous chain. An average molecule of the giant paraffin polymer called polyethylene has, perhaps, two thousand CH_2 groups and the shorthand formula $H - (CH_2)_{2000} - H$. For reasons we shall discuss in detail later, it is a tough, strong plastic rather than a brittle, waxy solid like triacontane.

I think you will agree that the mere formula $H - (CH_2)_{2000} - H$ does not give one a very good idea of the long-chain nature of the synthetic polymer polyethylene. To get a better visualization of something out of the ordinary, most scientists—and I am no exception—like to turn to a model. One of the models of polyethylene that I like is simple enough for you to make yourself. It is made by snapping together two thousand plastic "pop-it" beads of the kind used for necklaces and

* We will use the Celsius scale of temperature throughout this book. Devised in 1742 by the Swedish astronomer Anders Celsius and often called the centigrade scale, this system for designating temperature is used in scientific work throughout the world, and is in every-day use in all countries using the metric system. On the Celsius scale, the melting point of ice is at 0° and the boiling point of water is at 100°.

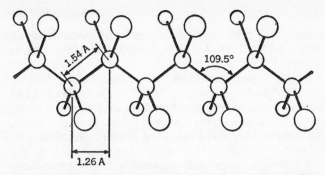

Fig. 3. When a carbon-carbon chain of atoms is fully stretched out, it has the zigzag arrangement shown in this figure. Since the distance between the centers of adjacent atoms is known to be 1.54 A (A is the abbreviation for the Angstrom unit, described in the text), and the angle between each bond and the next is known to be 109.5°, the distance between atoms along the direction of the chain is $1.54 \times \sin\left(\dfrac{109.5}{2}\right) = 1.26$ A.

bracelets of the costume-jewelry type. I have such a model at hand (Plate 2). It is about three-eighths inch in diameter and over eighty-three feet long when fully stretched out!

How do these dimensions correspond to the size of the actual polymer molecule? Well, real molecules are so small that it is inconvenient to describe their size in inches or centimeters. A special unit of length is used to describe distances comparable to molecular sizes. This is the Angstrom unit, abbreviated A, named after A. J. Ångström, a Swedish physicist of the nineteenth century. One A is one ten-billionth of a meter, or 1/100,000,000 of a centimeter. Since there are about 2.5 centimeters in an inch, it takes some 250,000,000 A to make one inch.

Now the length of the bond between two carbon atoms is 1.54 A, measured between the centers of the two atoms. As indicated in Figure 3, this corresponds to a distance of 1.26 A along the direction of the chain between each pair of atoms. For our polyethylene molecule with two thousand atoms and therefore 1999 $C-C$ bonds (or, to a good enough approximation, two thousand bonds), this means the fully stretched length of the chain is $2000 \times 1.26 = 2540$ A or $2540/100,000,000$ centimeter.

In our model, the length of the chain is 83 feet, or $83 \times 12 \times 2.54$ centimeters, which is just about 2540 centimeters. So in length our model is magnified just about 100,000,000 times over the real molecule it represents. (Of course, the model does not portray the zigzags of the actual chain.)

Assigning a meaningful diameter to the polymer chain is not easy for the chemists, but it must be of the order of magnitude of 1 A. A 100,000,000 magnification of this figure is one centimeter, or about three-eighths inch, just the diameter of the model.

So our model has about the same ratio of length to diameter as the hundred-million-times smaller molecule of polyethylene. We shall see later that the flexibility or wriggliness of the model is also characteristic of the actual polymer chains.

I should point out that a 100,000,000-times magnification is *very* large: It corresponds approximately to the difference between one second and three years! Thus real molecules, even the giant ones we call polymers, are very tiny indeed!

At this point, let's consider the weight of a polymer molecule. You may know that every atom in our world has a definite weight and (except for isotope effects, which do not concern us) all atoms of the same kind have the same weight. These weights are very small. A single hydrogen atom, for example, weighs only about $1/17,000,000,000,000,000,000,000,000$ ounce! To avoid talking in terms of such small numbers, we usually call the weight of a hydrogen atom 1 and express the weight of all other atoms relative to the weight of the hydrogen atom. Thus, on this scale, carbon has an *atomic weight* of 12, oxygen 16, and so on. These numbers are not quite exact, but this need not concern us.

Turning now to our typical polyethylene molecule $H - (CH_2)_{2000} - H$ and neglecting the two end hydrogen atoms compared to the rest of the chain, we assign a *molecular weight* of $12 + 1 + 1 = 14$ to the CH_2 group, and a molecular weight of $2000 \times 14 = 28,000$ to the entire molecule.

Both the molecular weight and the number of similar units repeated in our model chain are typical. Polymers usually have between a few hundred and a few thousand repeating sequences of atoms. Since many polymers have larger repeating units than ethylene, typical polymer molecular weights are between ten thousand and a few million.

WHAT HAS ALL THIS TO DO WITH PHYSICS?

At this stage you may be wondering what relation there can be between the structure of giant molecules and physics. It is true that chemistry as well as physics plays an important part in polymer science, and for a long time the chemistry of polymers was the predominant aspect of these materials being studied.

But this is no longer the case. In fact, as the chemistry of polymers has become better and better understood, scientists active in the field have become convinced that in the future their physics will become more and more important. In my opinion, the most exciting advances in polymer science in the next few years will involve the application of the laws of physics to modify the structures of the polymers we already have to produce new materials, rather than the development of entirely new chemical substances. This is perhaps natural, since it is well recognized that the end uses of polymers are almost all dependent on their physical, rather than their chemical, properties.

Finally, the borderlines between the branches of science continue to become more and more vague. Much of what I teach to college students of chemistry today was taught as physics when I was a student. Much of what I say in this book could equally well be called either chemical physics or physical chemistry. The names are not important; the ideas are.

Chapter 2

HOW SYNTHETIC POLYMERS
ARE MADE

The question of how man makes the giant molecules of plastics, fibers, and rubbers is one that, surprisingly, did not receive an answer until many years after some of these materials were in widespread commercial use. Although, as we saw in Chapter 1, "Bakelite" was produced as early as 1907, it was not until the studies of the American chemists W. H. Carothers in the early 1930s and Paul J. Flory a few years later that scientists achieved a clear understanding of the processes of *polymerization*—that is, the conversion of small molecules into polymers.

Many of the details of polymerization are of interest only to chemists, and we shall not delve into the subject deeply. But we shall examine a few principles that can aid our understanding, in later chapters, of some facts about the structure of polymer molecules.

If we wanted to trace the genealogy (so to speak) of a polymer back to its beginnings, we would have to start with the very simplest substances we know, and explore many chemical reactions before we got to the actual processes of making giant molecules. There was once a widely publicized claim that nylon is made from coal, air, and water. True, in the sense that the atoms of carbon from coal, nitrogen from air, hydrogen from water, and oxygen from air or water are the same ones occurring in the nylon molecule, but nobody ever made nylon by mixing coal, air, and water together in any kind of special apparatus!

Actually, the polymerization step, converting small molecules into big ones, combines substances called *monomers* (meaning one part) into polymers (meaning, as we have seen, many parts). So the logical place for us to start is with the monomers. Many of these are themselves quite complex molecules, but they have the common properties that they are small compared to polymers and that they are chemically reactive in some way (and again we will not be concerned with details) so that they can be joined together in long chains. The number of monomers joined together to make a polymer is called the *degree of polymerization* of that molecule.

At this point it is convenient to note that there are two rather different kinds of polymerization processes, from the physical point of view, which are best discussed separately. I shall call them *stepwise* polymerization and *chain* polymerization, names that are descriptive of the ways in which the processes take place.

STEPWISE POLYMERIZATION

The monomers used in stepwise polymerization are characterized by having a chemically active group on each end. These groups can join together, linking two monomers to form a double molecule known as a *dimer*. Dimers can react with monomers or other dimers to give still larger molecules. Step by step, we are on our way to producing a polymer.

Forgetting the chemistry, let us think of the monomers as small but powerful magnets. In this model, the two reactive ends are the north and south poles of the magnet. The process of polymerization starts with a mixture of these magnets, scrambled randomly together on a table, as depicted schematically in Figure 4. "Polymerization" begins when someone starts to shake the table; some of the magnets slide about and hit others, and a few become joined together in pairs. At a later time a few of the single and paired magnets have joined into longer chains, while toward the end of the "reaction" most of the magnets are strung together in the analog of a polymer molecule.

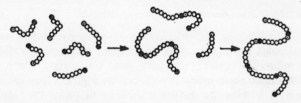

Fig. 4. In stepwise polymerization, any two small molecules can react to give a longer chain. These, in turn, can react together, and eventually a polymer chain is formed when all or nearly all possibility of reaction is exhausted.

The essential features of this experiment, which you can do yourself, duplicate those of stepwise polymerization. A typical monomer for this kind of polymerization is the substance $H_2N(CH_2)_5COOH$, an amino acid. On polymerization it gives one of the familiar nylons. The H_2N- group is called an amine group, and the atoms $-COOH$ make the molecule an acid; here these two reactive groups are joined to the opposite ends of a five-carbon paraffin chain.

It is actually not necessary that the H_2N- and $-COOH$ groups be on the same molecule; I have chosen this example because it simplifies the discussion to follow. Another familiar nylon—in fact, the commercial product resulting directly from Carothers' studies—is made from equal numbers of the molecules $H_2N(CH_2)_6NH_2$ and $HOOC(CH_2)_4COOH$.

In the polymerization process, the amine and acid groups join together, but split off the atoms of a molecule of water in the process:

$$-CO \boxed{OH + H} \overset{\displaystyle H}{\underset{\displaystyle |}{-N-}} \rightarrow -CONH- + H_2O$$

Here I have written the two hydrogen atoms on the amine group separately to show that one of them is split off, along with the atoms $-OH$ from the acid, as indicated by the dotted rectangle. What is left joins together to form the $-CONH-$ group, which is known as the peptide group or linkage. It is a very important constituent of proteins as well as the class of synthetic polymers we call the nylons.

We can now write the complete reaction for making nylon. This takes place when a large number, x, of the monomers is joined together, after many intermediate steps, to make a polymer molecule with degree of polymerization x:

$$x \ H_2N(CH_2)_5COOH \rightarrow$$
$$H[HN(CH_2)_5CO]_xOH + (x-1) \ H_2O$$

In the reaction, $x-1$ molecules of water are split out, with another $H-$ and $-OH$ remaining as parts of H_2N- and $-COOH$ groups forming the two ends of the polymer chain.

The presence of these unreacted end groups provides the means for both following the progress of the polymerization and finding the value of the degree of polymerization x. It is possible to measure the number of these groups remaining in the reaction mixture at any time by chemical methods. If we call N the number of, say, $-COOH$ groups remaining at a given time, and N_0 the original number, the ratio of these two, N/N_0, is a measure of how far the reaction has progressed. It is usual to define the *extent of reaction, p,* as the fraction of $-COOH$ groups used up, or as the probability (or chance) that a specific $-COOH$ has been used up; the two definitions are equivalent. If p is the fraction of $-COOH$ groups used up, then $(1-p)$ is the fraction remaining, N/N_0.

Now if there are N $-COOH$ groups remaining, there must be just N molecules, for each polymer molecule contains just one unreacted $-COOH$ group. Since the N_0 monomers originally present are now combined to form N molecules, the number of monomers per molecule must be N_0/N. This is the degree of polymerization, x, and the analysis of the preceding paragraph gives us a relationship between the degree of polymerization and the extent of reaction, p: $x = 1/(1-p)$.

This simple relation, sometimes called Carothers' equation, tells us that stepwise polymerizations must be carried to high extents of reaction in order to produce high polymer molecules. For example, to produce the nylon of the sort we have been talking about with molecules big enough to spin into synthetic fibers, x must be at least 100, and hence p must be about 0.99. Ninety-nine out of every 100 —COOH groups must have undergone reaction to achieve this result.

Degree of polymerization and molecular weight, which we saw defined in Chapter 1, are closely related: One finds the molecular weight of a polymer molecule by multiplying the degree of polymerization by the molecular weight of the monomer used—or, more strictly speaking, the molecular weight of that part of the monomer that gets incorporated into the polymer chain. Thus, if we consider the polymerization of the amino acid $H_2N(CH_2)_5COOH$ to a nylon with degree of polymerization 100, the molecular weight of this polymer will be 100 times the molecular weight of the atoms $-NH(CH_2)_5CO-$. Assigning the usual numbers $H = 1$, $C = 12$, $N = 14$, and $O = 16$, this fragment has a molecular weight of 113, and one hundred of these have a molecular weight of 11,300. To this we should add 18 for the H— and —OH making up the end groups on the polymer chain. But, as we will see in later chapters, we cannot measure polymer molecular weights accurately enough to distinguish this small amount, so it is often neglected. We would say that this nylon had a molecular weight of 11,300.

CHAIN POLYMERIZATION

The second major type of polymerization reaction we shall consider starts with a different sort of monomer, called an *unsaturated* molecule. In this type of substance, a pair of carbon atoms is connected together by what is known as a double bond. The simplest material of this type is the gas ethylene, whose formula is $H_2C = CH_2$. It is the monomer from which the plastic polyethylene is made.

The carbon-to-carbon double bond in unsaturated molecules is less stable than the other chemical bonds we have been discussing. These materials react readily with a wide variety of substances. With the proper "triggering" or *initiation*, for example, the double bond can be broken apart to give a highly reactive molecule, which we can indicate very schematically as $-CH_2CH_2-*$, where the asterisk indicates the extra energy or reactivity of the new molecule. In practice, the triggering action comes from an *initiator* molecule, which we will designate only as R. This initiator becomes attached to the ethylene so that the reactive material that is formed is better represented as $R-CH_2-CH_2-*$.

This process of initiation has in fact started a chain that can grow into a polymer molecule by a series of similar steps called *propagation*. The compound written above can react with another monomer (ethylene in our example), breaking its double bond, and adding it onto the reactive end to give $R-CH_2-CH_2-CH_2-CH_2-*$. This process can continue, usually quite rapidly, for many steps. After x steps have taken place, the result is a polymer molecule that is still very reactive: $R-(CH_2CH_2)_x-*$.

Such a material is of no value as a polymer because of its great reactivity. The chain polymerization process must be ended by a *termination* step. This takes place when two of the reactive molecules I have just described collide and react with each other. I will not trouble you with the details, except to say that the excess energy of the two molecules is used up in the collision, and normal polyethylene of the sort we described in Chapter 1 is formed.

As Figure 5 suggests, the sequence of initiation, propagation, and termination in chain polymerization takes place so rapidly that, in looking at a polymerizing mixture, one would see only monomer that had not yet reacted and polymer that had already been formed. Only one out of many millions of molecules examined would be caught in the growth process in a typical case.

Two consequences of this mechanism of polymer for-

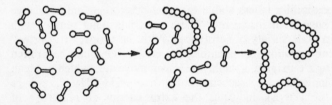

Fig. 5. In chain polymerization, the only growth reaction is the addition of monomers one at a time to reactive growing chains. Since the growth reaction usually takes place quite rapidly when started, one sees at intermediate stages only a mixture of monomers and large molecules.

mation are important to note. First, the polymer made in chain processes has a high degree of polymerization right from the beginning; it is not necessary to carry the reaction nearly to completion in order to get large molecules, as is true in stepwise polymerization. A second important difference between the two methods is that, unlike the situation in stepwise polymerization where any two molecules in the mixture can join together, the only growth reaction in chain polymerization is that in which a monomer molecule adds onto the end of a reactive growing chain.

SOME PROBLEMS IN GEOMETRY

As soon as we consider the chain polymerization of monomers slightly more complicated than ethylene, we find that in the simplified explanations of the last section we have overlooked some points of interest in the structure of high polymers.

Consider the polymerization of the monomer vinyl chloride. The term "vinyl" is used to describe monomers in which one of the hydrogens of ethylene is replaced by another atom or group of atoms. Vinyl chloride has the structure $CH_2 = CHCl$, where the chlorine atom Cl is introduced in this way. How does this molecule, whose ends are not alike, enter the growing chain?

Without getting too complicated, we can consider three possibilities. Let's call one end of the monomer, say the one with two hydrogens, its "head," and the other end, its "tail." Then it might be that it is always easier for one end of the monomer to add to the growing chain, producing a regular head-to-tail structure for poly(vinyl chloride) like this:

$$
\begin{array}{cccccccc}
H & H & H & H & H & H & H & H \\
| & | & | & | & | & | & | & | \\
\ldots - C - C - C - C - C - C - C - C - \ldots \\
| & | & | & | & | & | & | & | \\
H & Cl & H & Cl & H & Cl & H & Cl
\end{array}
$$

where the dots indicate that the chain extends in both directions beyond the section I have drawn.

Another possibility is that the monomers like to alternate in head-to-head, tail-to-tail fashion like this:

$$
\begin{array}{cccccccc}
H & H & H & H & H & H & H & H \\
| & | & | & | & | & | & | & | \\
\ldots - C - C - C - C - C - C - C - C - \ldots \\
| & | & | & | & | & | & | & | \\
H & Cl & Cl & H & H & Cl & Cl & H
\end{array}
$$

A third possibility is that it does not matter which way the monomer goes in, and the polymer chain is a random mixture of monomer units, some of which have added head-to-tail and others head-to-head, tail-to-tail.

It is not easy to learn enough about the structures of polymer chains to decide which of these possibilities is favored, but in those cases that have been studied the answer is always the same. The head-to-tail sequence is overwhelmingly favored, and only occasionally does a monomer get turned around and add onto the chain "backward."

Our shorthand method of writing polymer chain structures has disguised another series of possible structures that have become very important in recent years. To understand them, we must look again at Figure 1, which showed that in methane, the four bonds of the carbon atom are directed toward the four corners of a tetrahedron. The situation is not changed very much in the chains of vinyl polymers, so that a better approximation to the real structure of a polyethylene chain would be to draw it as the ball-and-stick model of Figure 3 rather than with the shorthand two-dimensional notation we have been using.

Now consider poly(vinyl chloride) again. Using the head-to-tail arrangement we know to be correct, we can still write three different structures for this chain, as indicated in Figure 6. These structures were first described by Giulio Natta in 1955. (Natta, a contemporary Italian

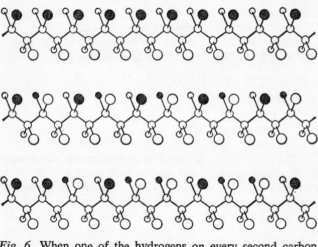

Fig. 6. When one of the hydrogens on every second carbon atom in the polyethylene chain is replaced with a chlorine, the structure is that of poly(vinyl chloride). Now, because of the possibility of having the different three-dimensional arrangements shown in these models, three distinct structures can exist. The one drawn at the top, with all the chlorines (shaded) sticking out of the same side of the carbon-carbon chain, is called *isotactic*. The next, in which the chlorines alternate regularly, front and back, is known as *syndiotactic*, while the bottom, random structure is called *atactic*. Poly-(vinyl chloride) can be made in the syndiotactic or the atactic forms, while polypropylene, the polymer of $CH_2 = CH - CH_3$, is produced only in the isotactic form.

polymer scientist, shared the 1963 Nobel prize with his German colleague Karl Ziegler for their independent but related work on synthesizing polymers with these novel structures.)

Natta coined three new terms to describe these geometrically different chain structures, based on the Greek root -tactic, meaning order. He called the structure having all the chlorine (in this example) atoms on the same side of the carbon-carbon chain the *isotactic* structure; the regularly alternating structure, *syndiotactic;* and the random, disordered structure, *atactic,* meaning without order.

In recent years polymer scientists have learned how to make both isotactic and syndiotactic polymers, and have found that they have quite different properties from their atactic counterparts. In another chapter we will consider the origin and nature of these important consequences of geometrically regular chain structures.

The secrets of how to make isotactic or syndiotactic polymers are not yet fully understood, but the basic principle seems to be that the monomer must be held in a certain position, or orientation, with respect to the growing chain end, as it is added to the chain. Often, this appears to be accomplished by carrying out the polymerization on the surface of some solid material, where the monomer is held in the correct position by intermolecular forces.

BRANCHED AND NETWORK POLYMERS

So far, all of the polymers discussed, including those made by stepwise and by chain processes, can be described as *linear* polymers. That is, their chain structure continues in a single path from end to end, like a cross-country highway with no side roads along its length. But other classes of polymers can be made, some of which are very important industrially. As Figure 7 shows schematically, these include *branched* polymers and *network* polymers, sometimes called *crosslinked* polymers or crosslinked networks, for reasons that should be obvious.

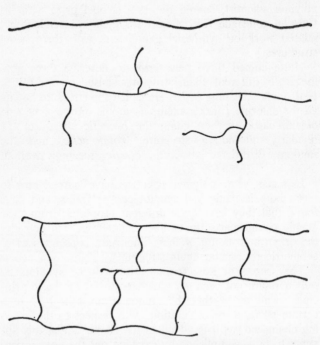

Fig. 7. This sketch shows the essential differences among linear, branched, and network or crosslinked polymer chains. A real crosslinked polymer could not, of course, be flattened down onto a plane, but has a three-dimensional structure.

There are several ways in which these more complex polymers can be made. I shall mention only one or two that find important commercial applications. Both branching and crosslinking, or network formation, can be introduced into polymers made by stepwise polymerization through the use of monomers having more than two reactive groups apiece. Whenever a monomer with, say, three reactive groups becomes part of a chain, a branch point is introduced, and with enough of this type of monomer, three-dimensional network structures will eventually be formed.

This is the way in which plastics like Leo Baekeland's "Bakelite," described in Chapter 1, are made. These substances are known as *thermosetting* polymers because the last stage in the polymerization, that of network formation or "setting," is carried out by the application of heat and pressure. This step takes place after the partially polymerized material is formed into the final shape it will have. The details of the structure of this sort of polymer are largely unknown, despite their commercial importance, both historically and at the present time, and we will not consider them further.

The crosslinking, or vulcanization, of rubber (another very old process) is a second example of network formation. Here, some double bonds are purposely left in the polymer molecules at the end of the chain polymerization process (by techniques we need not discuss). Later, again after the material is formed into its final shape, these double bonds are used up in other chain reactions that link together (hence, crosslink) the linear chain polymers into a network. If the process is stopped when only a few crosslinks have formed, the elastic material we call a typical rubber results. We will have a look at the interesting properties of rubbers in a later chapter. If the crosslinking reaction is continued, the plastic known as hard rubber, or ebonite, is formed. It is very much like the thermosetting plastics.

Chapter 3

RANDOMNESS IN THE MASSES
OF POLYMER MOLECULES

We have seen that polymers are quite different from ordinary substances because of their high molecular weights and unique long chain structure. Now let us examine another basic difference and see why it is important.

Most of the substances we use every day are what the chemists call "pure" materials. By this they mean that all of the molecules of a given material are exactly alike. This is true, for example, of the individual members of the paraffin family described in Chapter 1: All molecules of propane have the formula C_3H_8 and the structure shown in Figure 2.

What about polymers? Were we correct in calling polyethylene $H-(CH_2)_{2000}-H$? Are all its molecules exactly like this? If they were, it would require, first of all, that they all have exactly the same chain length. Can we predict anything about the chances of finding this from our study of polymerization processes in Chapter 2?

RANDOMNESS IN POLYMERIZATION PROCESSES

In the previous chapter we described several ways in which monomers are joined together to form polymer molecules. We saw, for example, that in chain polymerization, an active molecule was formed that could add monomers, one at a time, to its growing end, much as we might build our bead model of a polymer by taking one bead at a time from a pile on the table and adding it to the chain. The length of the chain or degree of polymerization is determined by how long we keep this up before stopping. Unless we run out of beads, this may occur at some random time depending on how tired we are, or whether it is time for lunch, or whether the telephone rings. If we were to make several bead models in this way, starting afresh every time we were interrupted, it is most unlikely that they would all have the same length.

An analogous situation exists in chain polymerization. The time at which a polymer chain ceases to grow, because its activity is destroyed, depends upon purely random events that cannot be controlled or even predicted in advance. Thus, just as in the model, it is extremely unlikely that all the polymer chains made at one time will have the same length.

Let us also look at stepwise polymerization. This technique corresponds, as we have seen, to starting our bead model by picking up two single beads from a pile, joining them, and putting the resulting two-bead chain (a dimer) back into the pile. If we keep reaching in and picking up beads or chains at random, joining them, and returning them, we will eventually have a wide variety of chains in the pile. Possibly there will be some single beads (monomers), some dimers, and some of every length of chain up to very long ones.

Again, the situation in the real polymerizing mixture of chemicals is quite similar. We do have conditions present in both kinds of polymerization processes that lead to a mixture of molecules with various chain lengths in a given polymer sample. This is surely different from ordinary substances in an important way. But how can we describe this distribution of chain lengths?

HOW MANY CHAINS OF EACH KIND?

In the simplest case—the only one we shall examine—the question of how many chains of each length are in a polymerizing mixture has the same answer for the two types of polymerizing systems, stepwise and chain. Let us think in terms of the mixture of chains of beads resulting from our analogy to stepwise polymerization. First, we need to distinguish two types of beads in the mixture: those that have already been connected to another bead, and those that have not (Figure 8).

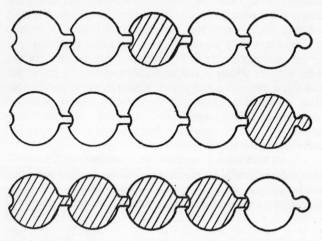

Fig. 8. The shaded bead in the top chain has already been connected to another one. In the middle chain the shaded bead has not yet been connected. The chain with five beads at the bottom has four connected (shaded) beads and one unconnected (unshaded) bead.

A little thought will show that we must consider the bead on the left-hand end of the figure as already connected if we are to say that only one more bead becomes connected every time one more connection is made.

Now suppose that we reach into the pile and pick up a single bead, which may or may not be part of a longer chain. What is the chance that we have picked up a bead that is connected to another?

This question has a simple answer. If the beads were randomly mixed, our chance of getting a "connected" one is just equal to the fraction of the beads that are already connected. If exactly two-thirds of the beads are connected, we can expect on the average to pick up a connected one exactly twice out of every three trials, and of course to pick up one not yet connected one-third of the time. We can state this result in more general terms by saying that if p is the fraction of the beads that have been connected, p is also the chance or probability of finding a connected bead, and $1 - p$ is the probability of finding an unconnected bead. Note that p is just the extent of reaction that we defined in Chapter 2.

The next step is just about as easy. Suppose that we dip into the pile and pull out a chain of five beads. What is the chance of our doing this? To answer this question we have to know how to find the chance of doing several things at once. What we did in this case was to pick up four connected beads and one unconnected one all at the same time. The chance of doing this is obtained by multiplying together the probabilities of finding each of the beads in five separate trials. Thus, using the probabilities we discovered above for getting a connected or an unconnected bead, the chance of finding a chain of five beads is

$$p \times p \times p \times p \times (1 - p) \text{ or } p^4(1 - p)$$

Let us now write this result in a more general way, not restricting ourselves to five beads. Note that a chain of any length, say x, has one less than x connected beads but only one unconnected bead. The chance of finding such a chain is, therefore, $p^{x-1}(1 - p)$.

We can look at this experiment in another way. If we knew how many chains of all lengths were in our pile, and how many of them had five beads, we could say right away what the chance of picking a chain of five beads would be: It would be just the fraction of five-bead chains in the mixture. For a chain of x beads we can write this fraction as N_x/N, where N_x is the number of chains x beads long and N is the total number of chains in the pile.

THE MOLECULAR-WEIGHT DISTRIBUTION

We now have two expressions for the chance of finding a chain of x beads in our pile, and we can set them equal:

$$N_x/N = p^{x-1}(1 - p)$$

This equation lets us calculate, for any chain length x, the fractional number of chains having that length. Thus, it provides the answer to our original question of how many chains of each length are to be found in the mixture. Of course, the result applies equally well to the case of a polymerizing mixture of molecules as to our bead model.

It is more convenient, in thinking about the stepwise polymerization process, to eliminate N, which is the total number of chains in the mixture at the point where a fraction p of the reactive groups on the molecules has been used up, and work instead with the number of monomers (single beads, in our model) that was present at the start. If we call this number N_0, and remember that at a later time when p molecules have reacted, $1 - p$ are left and are distributed one to each of the N chains present, it is easy to see that $N = N_0(1 - p)$. Putting this into our earlier equation and solving for N_x gives

$$N_x = N_0(1 - p)^2 p^{x-1}$$

This is the equation that tells us, for any extent of reaction, p, the number of chains of every degree of polymerization x that is present. For $p = 0.99$, that is, the case where 99 per cent of all the possible links have been made, a plot of this equation gives the graph of Figure 9.

Quite surprisingly, this graph tells us that there are more molecules of unreacted monomer in the mixture than of any other chain length! This is true, in fact, for any extent of reaction, p. The next most numerous kind of molecule is the dimer, followed by the trimer, and so on in order of ascending chain length.

This strange fact is quite characteristic, but its importance is lessened by the very small weight of the monomer compared to that of the longer chains. To put it another way, we should really be asking a different question: We should be inquiring about the relative weights, not numbers, of molecules of each kind. It is simple to change our earlier result to give this quantity.

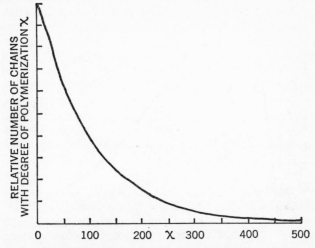

Fig. 9. This figure shows the relative number of chains of length x, for all values of x (the number of beads in the chain). The case illustrated is for a condensation or step-reaction polymerization in which 99 per cent of all the molecules have reacted. That is, the extent of reaction, p, is 0.99. Of course, the curve does not stop at the right-hand end of this graph but continues, getting lower and lower, to much higher values of x.

The weight of a chain of x beads is just x times the weight of a single bead, and the weight of all the chains of length x is, therefore, xN_x times the weight of a single bead. Similarly, the weight of all the beads is N_0 times the weight of a single bead. The ratio of these, xN_x/N_0, is the fraction of the total weight arising from chains of length x. If we designate this W_x and substitute into our previous formula, we obtain the result that

$$W_x = x(1-p)^2 p^{x-1}$$

A plot of W_x for all values of x at the extent of reaction $p = 0.99$ is shown in Figure 10. Now we see that the very short polymer chains do not contribute so heavily to the weight distribution of chain lengths, despite the larger

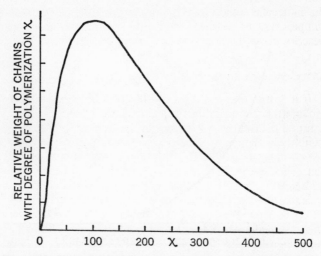

Fig. 10. When we consider the relative weights, rather than numbers, of molecules of chain length x, this molecular-weight distribution curve results. This is also drawn for the case when $p = 0.99$.

numbers of these very small molecules in the mixture. Instead, there is a "most probable" chain length or degree of polymerization, accounting for a larger fraction of the total weight of the sample than any other. In this example, the "most probable" chain length—at the maximum in the curve—is one hundred units.

But the most important feature of our analysis of the statistical nature of polymerization is that the polymers we have talked about, and in fact *all* synthetic polymers known to man (and some naturally occurring ones too) *always* contain a broad distribution of chain lengths. Since the weight of the polymer molecule—its molecular weight —is just proportional to the length of its chain or its degree of polymerization, we can restate our conclusion to say that every sample of synthetic polymer ever made contains molecules having a broad distribution of molecular weights. This is another unique feature of polymers, and one that accounts for many of their outstanding properties. We may, however, find it difficult to learn all about the molecular-weight distributions of all sorts of polymer samples. Let us look for some simple quantities that can describe these distributions in a shorthand way.

AVERAGE MOLECULAR WEIGHTS

If it is true that every sample of polymer (except some biological material such as proteins and DNA) contains a broad distribution of molecular weights, and since any sample big enough to measure contains a very large number of molecules, then it must be that the only thing we can ever observe is an *average* property of this group of molecules. In practice this does not present any difficulty, because these average values are reproduced well from one part to another of a large quantity of material made in the same way. This is not surprising, since a little calculation will show that we do indeed always deal with very large numbers of polymer molecules in every sample that we handle. One ounce of our typical polyethylene (Chapter 1) with an average molecular weight of 28,000 contains about 600,000,000,000,000,000,000,000 molecules!

What are some of these average quantities? For the moment, let us restrict our interest to the weight of the molecule, and rephrase our question to ask what kinds of average molecular weight can be measured, and what they mean.

The concept of an average quantity that is most familiar is, I think, the one in which we consider the number of objects in a group, and divide the property of the group by this number to obtain the average property per object. Thus, if we have a pile of ten stones weighing one hundred pounds, the average weight per stone is 100/10 or ten pounds. In terms of molecules, then, if we can find a way to count the number of molecules in a sample, and can weigh the sample, we can in this way determine the average weight per molecule. Since this kind of average is based on the number of molecules in the sample, we call it the number-average molecular weight and give it the symbol $\bar{M}_n$, the bar indicating that the quantity is an average, and the subscript n indicating that it is the number average.

If, as before, we let the total number of molecules present in a sample be designated N, and the weight of the sample W, we can write

$$\bar{M}_n = \frac{W}{N}$$

Can we express this in a more useful way? Let us talk again about the individual molecules of chain length x, remembering that we designated the number of such chains as N_x. The total number of molecules, N, is just the sum of all these N_x's for all values of x that we have in the mixture:

$$N = N_1 + N_2 + \ldots + N_x + \ldots$$

We have a shorthand way of writing this using the Greek capital letter sigma, Σ, as a summation sign:

$$N = \Sigma N_x$$

and we sometimes indicate the range of values of x to be included in the sum by writing them below and above the summation sign: If we want to add up the numbers of molecules with values of x between 10 and 20 we could write

$$\sum_{x=10}^{x=20} N_x$$

If we wish to count all the molecules we should let x take on all possible values between one and infinity:

$$N = \sum_{x=1}^{x=\infty} N_x$$

Usually we can omit these limits when it is clear what is meant.

Now the weight of a single molecule of chain length x

can be called M_x. Then the weight of all N_x of these molecules is $N_x M_x$, and the total weight of the sample is just the sum of this product for all x:

$$W = \Sigma \, N_x M_x$$

Then we can write the number-average molecular weight as

$$\bar{M}_n = \frac{\Sigma \, N_x M_x}{\Sigma \, N_x}$$

It is not so difficult to understand the significance of $\bar{M}_n$ because we are so familiar with the counting and averaging process that it represents. In Chapter 5 we shall explore ways of counting molecules and thus of measuring $\bar{M}_n$.

Of course, we can also talk about the average degree of polymerization of a polymer sample, $\bar{x}$. We can write down the formula for the number-average degree of polymerization, $\bar{x}_n$, as

$$\bar{x}_n = \frac{\Sigma \, x N_x}{\Sigma \, N_x}$$

just by replacing M_x by x. Another way of thinking of this quantity is to ask how the N_0 monomers are distributed among N molecules, on the average. It must be that

$$\bar{x}_n = \frac{N_0}{N}$$

In addition, according to the equation $N = N_0(1-p)$ we derived on page 32, we can write

$$\bar{x}_n = \frac{1}{1-p}$$

Now this is just the same as the Carothers equation derived in Chapter 2, and it shows us that the degree of polymerization x we talked about at that time is really the number-average degree of polymerization $\bar{x}_n$.

There are several other types of averaging useful in polymer science. Perhaps the next most important average

beyond $\bar{M}_n$ is the one called the weight-average molecular weight, $\bar{M}_w$. The equation that defines this quantity is

$$\bar{M}_w = \frac{\Sigma\ N_x M_x^2}{\Sigma\ N_x M_x}$$

or

$$\bar{M}_w = \frac{\Sigma\ W_x M_x}{\Sigma\ W_x}$$

The formula for getting $\bar{M}_w$ can be written in terms of
the weights W_x of the chains in the same way that $\bar{M}_n$
can be written in terms of their numbers N_x. This different sort of average is important because each kind of
molecule contributes to the average in a way depending
on its mass as well as the amount of it in the mixture.
This is exactly what happens in some experiments we
shall learn about later. Thus $\bar{M}_w$ becomes important because it is a number that we can measure and that tells us
something more about the polymers in which we are interested.

HOW BROAD ARE POLYMER
MOLECULAR-WEIGHT DISTRIBUTIONS?

If we look at the equations for $\bar{M}_w$ and $\bar{M}_n$, we can
see that the value of the weight-average molecular weight
is always larger than that of the number average, except
for the case we said we could never get, where all the
molecules have exactly the same molecular weight. In
fact, as the distribution of molecular weights in the sample gets broader—that is, as more sorts of molecules of
different molecular weights appear in the sample—the values of $\bar{M}_w$ and $\bar{M}_n$ draw farther apart. For example, in
the molecular-weight distribution we described earlier for
polymers made by stepwise polymerization, $\bar{M}_w$ is twice
$\bar{M}_n$, as illustrated in Figure 11.

The synthetic polymers used for plastics, rubbers, and
fibers have a wide range of different types of molecular-
weight distributions. The ratio $\bar{M}_w / \bar{M}_n$ describing the

PLATE 1. This sketch of the molecule of methane, CH$_4$, is our best guess as to how it might actually look if we could see it, except that the molecule is probably more "fuzzed out" at its edges, so to speak, instead of having sharp boundaries.

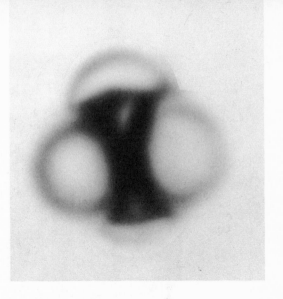

PLATE 2. A model of the synthetic polymer polyethylene, made by snapping two thousand pop-it beads together. Its dimensions, ⅜ inch in diameter and 83 feet long, make it a 100,000,000-times enlargement of an actual polyethylene molecule. Each bead represents a CH$_2$ group, and in the model of a chain of this length we can neglect the extra H atom on each end. The shorter groups at the bottom right represent octane (eight beads) and butane (four beads).

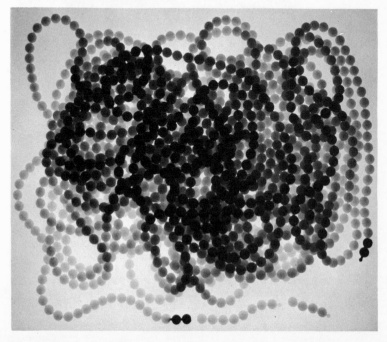

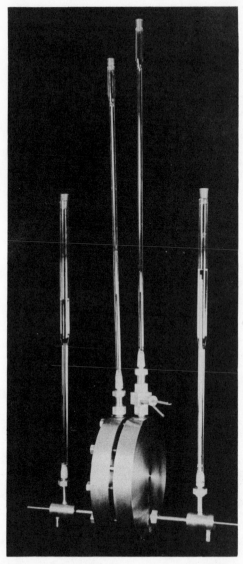

PLATE 3. This osmometer has a heavy metal cell about 20 cm in diameter. The two glass capillary tubes rising from the top of the cell are the measuring tubes; the other two are used for filling the osmometer and are closed off by valves when the osmotic pressure is measured. The osmotic membrane is placed between the two halves of the metal cell, just as the sketch of Figure 30 shows, before they are bolted tightly together. (From my *Textbook of Polymer Chemistry,* Interscience, 1957.)

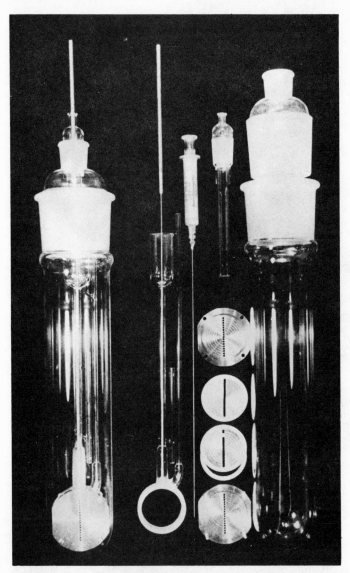

PLATE 4. Here is an osmometer that is simpler and smaller than the one shown in the previous plate. Two membranes are used, clamped by metal retainer plates to a small glass cell. The polymer solution is put into this through a filling tube, which is then closed; as the osmotic pressure develops, the liquid level rises in the capillary tube. The entire instrument is placed in a beaker or test tube containing the pure solvent; another section of capillary tube dipping into the solvent provides the reference level for measuring the osmotic pressure. (Courtesy of J. V. Stabin.)

PLATE 5. The high-speed automatic osmometer described in Figure 31. The solvent and solution cells, with the capillary and its trapped air bubble, are in the insulated chamber on the right; the "tower" in the middle holds the solvent cup, which moves up or down to seek the correct difference in liquid levels. (Courtesy of Hewlett-Packard Corp.)

PLATE 6. In this vapor-phase osmometer, the tops of the syringes for putting liquid droplets on the thermistors can be seen on top of the chamber at the left. On the right is the sensitive electronic equipment used to measure $\triangle r$, as described in the text. (Courtesy of Hewlett-Packard Corp.)

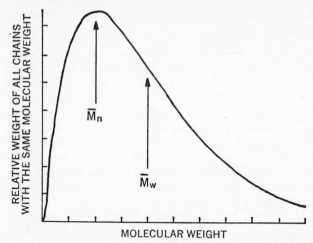

Fig. 11. In this typical molecular-weight distribution curve, the weight-average molecular weight, $\bar{M}_w$, is just twice the number-average molecular weight $\bar{M}_n$. The ratio of these two gives information about the breadth of the distribution curve, as illustrated here and in the two following figures.

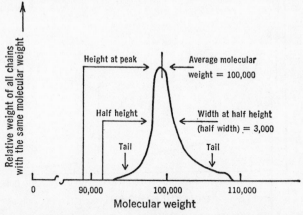

Fig. 12. The narrowest molecular-weight distribution curves we have been able to produce in synthetic polymers look about like this. The ratio $\bar{M}_w/\bar{M}_n$ describing the breadth of the curves is about 1.02. If all the molecules had the same molecular weight, this ratio would be exactly one, and the curve would be infinitely narrow instead of having the width shown.

breadth of the distribution curve can be as low as 1.02 or less, and as high as 50. It is difficult to draw curves like that of Figure 11 illustrating these very different sorts of distributions. The polymers with the narrowest distributions we know how to make—that is, those most nearly approaching the case in which all the molecules would have the same length, have distribution curves about like that sketched in Figure 12. At the moment these polymers have no great commercial value, but they are very useful as standard substances to test the various techniques for measuring the size and shape of giant molecules that I will describe later in this book.

At the other extreme, as my colleagues and I were able to demonstrate some years ago, one of our most useful

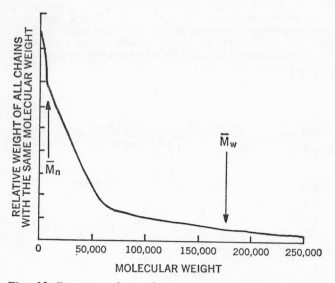

Fig. 13. By comparison, the important synthetic polymer polyethylene has a very broad distribution of molecular weights. In this sample, which my colleagues and I studied a few years ago, the ratio $\bar{M}_w/\bar{M}_n$ is about 30; even higher values are sometimes observed. In this sample we found polymer with molecular weight as low as 500 and as high as 1,500,000.

plastics, polyethylene, can have molecular-weight distributions in which the ratio $\bar{M}_w/\bar{M}_n$ is 30 or more. As Figure 13 suggests, the distribution curves of such samples are so flat as to be almost featureless.

To study the details of these molecular-weight distribution curves is an important and challenging task for the polymer scientist. As we shall see, the physical properties of synthetic polymers are to a great extent determined by their average molecular weights and the nature of their molecular-weight distribution curves. Only in recent years have we learned how to carry out the study of these properties rapidly and efficiently.

Chapter 4

RANDOMNESS IN THE SIZES
OF POLYMER MOLECULES

We have seen how polymers are different from ordinary
substances because they have a distribution of molecular
weights, and later on we shall explore the effect of this
distribution on the properties of important synthetic polymers. Now let us return to the nature of a single polymer
chain, and explore a new property: its size, or space-
filling behavior. You will remember that one of the im-
pressive characteristics of our "pop-it" bead model of a
synthetic polymer molecule was its extreme flexibility or
"wriggliness." If this is characteristic of the real molecule,
what does it tell us about synthetic polymers?

WHAT DO WE MEAN BY THE "SIZE"
OF A POLYMER MOLECULE?

At the beginning, I must emphasize that throughout this
chapter we will be talking about the *size* and not the *mass*
of a polymer molecule. These two things are quite different. For example, if we want to find the mass of our bead
model, we can put it on a scale and weigh it; if we ask
about its size, we are concerned instead with the amount
of space it takes up. Is it small enough to put in a pocket?
No. In a small box? Yes, possibly. But what will happen
if we throw it across the room onto the floor? Very likely,
it will uncoil and take up a lot more space, though its
mass hasn't changed.

This is what we mean by size: the amount of space the

chain takes up. I shall give you now the answer to the question of how much space a real polymer chain takes up, and we will see how this answer is obtained later in this chapter. To the best of our knowledge, when a real polymer molecule is mixed randomly with others like it, or when it is surrounded by small molecules—that is, when it is dissolved in a low-molecular-weight solvent—it expands into a randomly-coiling state much like that shown in Figure 14, rather than clumping tightly together. This property is a little difficult to show with our model because of the great difference in density between the model

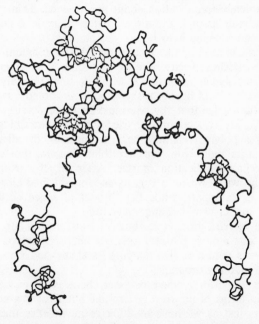

Fig. 14. This is a representation of what a randomly-coiling synthetic polymer chain might look like. It is calculated for a polyethylene chain of one thousand links, just half the size of the one we have been using as a model, and it suffers from being a two-dimensional drawing of a three-dimensional arrangement of the chain. (Courtesy of L. R. G. Treloar and the Oxford University Press.)

and the air surrounding it, but if we were to throw the bead model into a large swimming pool or pond, we would see it behave in the same way.

Figure 14 shows, then, that in its normal random-coiling state, the polymer molecule is very much spread out, or extended. The origin of its ability to assume extended arrangements, or *conformations,* like the one illustrated, lies in the flexibility of the bonds holding the chain atoms together. As we saw earlier, these are carbon-carbon single bonds in polyethylene, and to a large extent in most other synthetic polymers as well. To a first approximation, which can be corrected later, we shall assume that there is completely free rotation about these bonds. That is, we shall start by assuming that the polymer chain is as flexible as we can imagine it to be.

Before exploring the results of this bold assumption, we must decide exactly how we are going to measure the size of a polymer molecule. It won't do to say merely that our model would fit into a shoebox, or is spread out over a nine-by-twelve-foot rug; we must be more precise.

There are two commonly used ways of describing the size of a polymer chain. One is to measure the distance between its ends. Now you may think that this would not be a reliable indication of size. After all, if our model were thrown down on a rug, its ends might land close together or far apart, while the amount of space occupied by the model would change very little.

This is true, of course, but we must remember that, unlike our model, the real polymer chain, dissolved in a solvent, is continuously changing its shape and size as it floats randomly around.

Thus, even for a single polymer chain, we must always think in terms of an *average* size and shape over a period of time, just as we have to think of an average mass or molecular weight for a group of chains. On the average, the distance between the ends of a randomly-coiling polymer chain is a good measure of how big it is.

Another way of measuring the size of a polymer chain is through what is known as its radius of gyration. This is just the average distance of all the chain atoms from the center of gravity of the entire molecule. The calculation of the radius of gyration is described in Figure 15.

In this book, we shall use the one of these two measures of the size of polymer chains that is more closely related to what we are discussing. As we shall see in the next section, the end-to-end distance is closely related to the calculation of the size of a chain from its randomly-coiling behavior. Later on, we shall see that the radius of gyration is directly related to some things we can measure. For linear chains (but not branched or network polymers, which have more than two ends), these two are closely related: The end-to-end distance is equal to the radius of gyration multiplied by the square root of 6 (about 2.5).

There are other ways, too, of measuring the size of a polymer chain—for example, in terms of the volume it occupies. We shall meet some of these measures later in this chapter.

THE "RANDOM-FLIGHT" MODEL
OF A POLYMER CHAIN

There is a famous mathematical problem, known for a hundred years, which bears closely on the size of polymer molecules. It is the following:

Suppose that a blindfolded man were placed in the center of a football field. Suppose he took one step, and then turned around to a new direction, at random, and then took another step. Then suppose he turned again, to another direction unrelated to the way he moved the previous time, took another step, turned again, and so on. The problem is: How far from his starting place would he have gone after a large number of steps?

Do you see the relation between this problem and a polymer? It's easier to recognize if we think in three dimensions rather than two—maybe we should have talked about a blindfolded bumblebee, free to hover and fly in any direction. That would be a rather flippant statement of the random-flight problem solved by the famous English physicist Lord Rayleigh just one hundred years ago, and it gives a way of calculating the distance between the

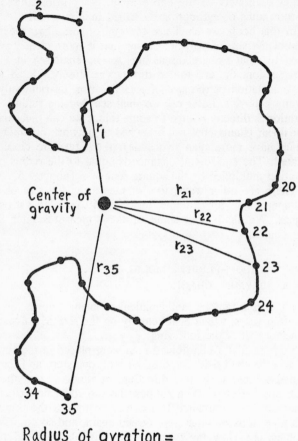

Radius of gyration =

$$\sqrt{r_1^2 + \cdots + r_{21}^2 + r_{22}^2 + r_{23}^2 + \cdots + r_{35}^2}$$

Fig. 15. To calculate the radius of gyration of a polymer chain, first find its center of gravity. Then, measure the distance from this point to each of the atoms in the chain. Square all these distances, add the squares up, and take the square root of the sum.

ends of a polymer chain if we assume, as we stated in the previous section, that each bond is completely flexible.

For the purposes of the random-flight calculation, let us assume that the polymer chain is made up of thin bonds, all of the same length, joining together tiny atoms, so that we can neglect the thickness of both the atoms and the bonds. Let us also assume that the two bonds attached to a single atom are free to take any directions we wish, corresponding to complete flexibility (Figure 16). Then, the answer for the distance between the beginning and end of a random flight of many equal steps is also the

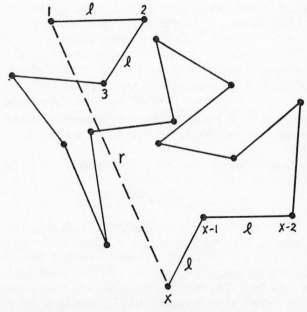

Fig. 16. The random-flight calculation asks what is the distance between the ends of an imaginary polymer molecule made up of x minutely small atoms joined by links of length l. It assumes that the direction of each of these links is chosen at random and does not depend in any way on the direction of the previous link, or any other.

answer for the distance between the ends of our polymer chain.

We need not derive this answer, but the result is interesting and important: If the number of bonds in the chain is x and the length of each bond is l, then the average end-to-end distance of the chain is l times the *square root* of x. The unexpected part of this result is that, while the size of the chain is proportional to the length of the bonds in it, the chain grows only in proportion to the square root of the number of bonds. Thus, to double the end-to-end size of a polymer chain, we would have to take four times as many atoms.

Before illustrating this with numbers, let me define what I mean by the *average* end-to-end distance. It turns out that this measure of the size of the chain has to be obtained by making calculations of many different random flights. For each one, the end-to-end distance (let us call it r) is squared, and then all the quantities r^2 are averaged (let us call $\overline{r^2}$ the average of all the r^2's), and finally the square root of the average of all the r^2's is taken. This quantity, $\sqrt{\overline{r^2}}$, is known as the root-mean-square end-to-end distance, and this is the kind of average that is required.

The mathematical equation describing the result of the random-flight calculation is, then,

$$\sqrt{\overline{r^2}} = l \sqrt{x}$$

For a polyethylene-like chain with 2000 bonds each 1.54 A long, but with the assumptions of infinitesimally small atoms and completely free rotation required by the random-flight calculation, we can substitute 2000 for x and 1.54 for l. The random-flight root-mean-square end-to-end distance of such a chain (which I want to designate $\sqrt{\overline{r_f^2}}$ to distinguish it from other kinds of end-to-end distances we shall derive later) is

$$\sqrt{\overline{r_f^2}} = 1.54 \sqrt{2000} \text{ A}$$
$$= 69 \text{ A}$$

Only 69 A! Yet the entire length of the chain, known as its *contour length,* the sum of the lengths of all its bonds, is 2000×1.54 A $= 3080$ A! In terms of our model, magnified so that 1 A $= 1$ centimeter, the distance between the ends of the chain is only 69 cm or a little over two feet. At this stage, it doesn't look as if our polymer chain takes up so much space after all.

FROM RANDOM FLIGHT
TO REAL POLYMER MOLECULE

In point of fact, the random-flight calculation does underestimate the size of the polymer chain rather badly. The assumptions that we had to make are not realistic, and we must examine them and correct for them, one by one.

First of all, we have forgotten that we said in Chapter 1 that the bonds in a carbon-carbon chain are *not* free to take any direction with respect to one another, but the angle between successive bonds has a constant value of about 109.5°. This has the effect of reducing the flexibility of the chain somewhat, and it is easy to show that it leads to an increase in $\sqrt{\bar{r}^2}$ by a factor of the square root of two, or 1.4. Thus, keeping all the flexibility of the chain except for the constant bond angle, as indicated in Figure 17, leads to an increase in the end-to-end distance from 69 A to about 98 A. In our model, this would be about $3\frac{1}{4}$ feet. It was on this basis, also, that in Chapter 1 we figured the fully-extended length of the model to be eighty-three feet.

Next let us examine the assumption of completely free rotation around carbon-carbon bonds, maintaining the proper bond angles. As Figure 17 shows, this means that carbon atom number 4 would have the same chance of being found anywhere on the circle shown. But it is known that this is wrong, because the effect of the hydrogen atoms on these carbons has to be taken into account, as shown in Figure 18. The effect of this local restriction on the freedom of rotation of the chain was calculated some

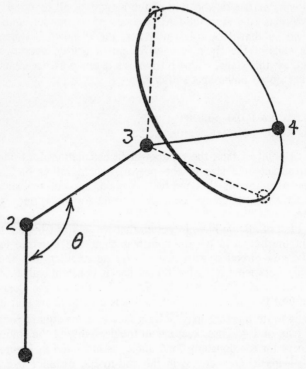

Fig. 17. A real polymer chain differs from the random-flight model in several respects. First of all, the angle between two successive bonds or links in the chain is fixed. For the carbon-carbon chain this angle, here labeled θ (the lower-case Greek letter theta), is about 109.5°. If, as the random-flight calculation assumes, there were completely free rotation about each of these bonds, then the carbon atom labeled 4 could be found with equal probability anywhere on the circle shown, for all points on this circle correspond to the correct value of θ. For each possible position of atom 4, the next carbon atom in the chain, which is not shown in the drawing, could have any one of many different locations on a similar circle. This explains why a polymer chain can have many different arrangements or conformations.

years ago by the American scientist Henry Eyring, among others; it adds another factor of about 1.25 to the end-to-end distance, bringing it up to some 124 A for a polyethylene chain of two thousand bonds.

Recently, Paul J. Flory has demonstrated the importance of still another effect in increasing the size of real polymer chains over that calculated as we have shown. This is the "pentane interference" effect illustrated in

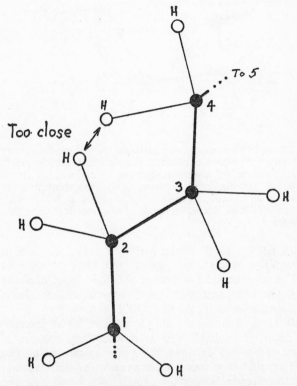

Fig. 18. If we remember that each of the carbon atoms in the polyethylene chain has two hydrogens attached to it, we can see that some arrangements of adjacent carbon atoms are not likely to occur because they put the hydrogen atoms too close together.

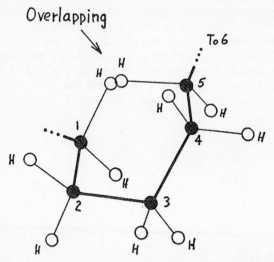

Fig. 19. A further important restriction to free rotation about the bonds in a polymer chain is the "pentane interference," which can occur for some arrangements of carbons five atoms apart. The volatile liquid pentane, C_5H_{12}, the shortest chain in the paraffin family described in Chapter 1 in which such interferences can occur, supplies the name for this phenomenon.

Figure 19, the result of the hydrogen atoms attached to carbons five atoms apart getting too close together in some arrangements of the chain. Another factor of about 1.5 is predicted, increasing the end-to-end distance for a two-thousand-atom chain to about 178 A.

All in all, then, we are able to account for an increase of a factor of around 2.6 to the random-flight root-mean-square end-to-end distance of a polyethylene chain. The resulting size is in good agreement with what we can measure directly by certain experiments I will describe later; we feel, therefore, that the major effects governing the size of real polymer chains are well understood.

But there is one more assumption in the random-flight calculation that must be looked into. This is related to the assumption of very small atoms. You see, the blindfolded man can step, or the bumblebee can fly, anywhere he wants to; it doesn't matter if he comes back to exactly the same place he had been before. The same would be true of the polymer chain if its atoms were very tiny, for two of them, or more, could occupy essentially the same place at one time. But this is not true for a real polymer chain. For the real molecule, all other segments of the chain must be excluded from the volume occupied by one of them. This means that all of the random-flight calculations—all of the conformations of the chain—in which two steps (two atoms) occur in the same place must be discarded. The question is, which ones and how many? And what effect does this have on the size of the molecule?

Here we simply do not know how to get the exact answers. The calculation of the excluded-volume effect is a major unsolved problem in polymer physics. The mathematics required is so difficult that I do not believe a solution will be found for many years to come. We do know, however, that more of the conformations in which the chain segments lie close together will have to be excluded, so the result will again lead to an increase in the size of the molecule. But we have gone about as far as theory allows, and to continue we must look at the results of experiments with dissolved polymer chains.

POLYMER-SOLVENT INTERACTIONS AND THE SIZES OF DISSOLVED POLYMERS

What do we mean by "dissolving" a polymer? What happens when a chunk of material containing many polymer chains is placed in the midst of a lot of small molecules making up a liquid?

Nothing happens, unless there is some reason why the segments of the polymer chains "prefer" to be surrounded by the small molecules rather than by their own kind. This can happen when strong enough intermolecular forces of the sort described in Chapter 1 can be developed. Then solvent molecules can slip in between the polymer chains, ultimately causing the mass of the polymer to break up into its separate molecules, each of them taking up the randomly-coiling arrangement we have been discussing, surrounded and interpenetrated by the small solvent molecules. We say that the polymer has dissolved.

The magnitude of the polymer-solvent interaction forces also has an effect on the size of the dissolved polymer chain. The stronger these forces are, the more the solvent molecules interpenetrate the polymer coil, and the more it expands to accommodate them. Thus, when the polymer is dissolved, the sizes its molecules assume are determined only in part by the numbers of atoms in the chain, x, the length of each chain bond, l, and such things as bond angles and hindrances to rotation discussed in the previous section. In part, the actual sizes of the chains reflect the magnitude of the polymer-solvent interaction forces.

These forces also depend on the temperature, becoming smaller at lower temperatures, and in most cases one can cool a polymer solution down to a point at which the polymer-solvent interaction forces just vanish. This is a rather special temperature, called the Flory temperature or the theta temperature because it is often designated by the Greek capital letter theta (Θ). Since we said that some interactions between polymer and solvent are needed to dissolve the giant molecules, the theta temperature must be near the point at which the polymer will no longer stay in solution. This is one way to recognize when the theta temperature has been reached; we will explore others in later chapters.

Paul J. Flory has shown that at the theta temperature, not only do the polymer-solvent interaction forces become zero, but as a result the size of the polymer chain becomes the same as it would be if the excluded-volume effect were absent. That is, as far as its average size is concerned, the chain *acts as if* some of its atoms could fall exactly on top of one another. Obviously, they cannot really do this, but the complicated mathematics of Flory's theories shows that the size of the chain would be the same in the absence of polymer-solvent interactions and in the absence of the excluded-volume effect.

A special name is given to this size: It is called the *unperturbed dimension* of the chain and is given the symbol $\sqrt{\overline{r_0^2}}$. As was described in the previous section, Flory and his co-workers have been able to calculate $\sqrt{\overline{r_0^2}}$ for some simple cases by adding the effects of constant bond angle and hindered rotation to the random-flight calculation. For polyethylene, for example, we saw that

$$\sqrt{\overline{r_0^2}} = 2.6 \ \sqrt{\overline{r_f^2}}$$

At temperatures above the theta point, the dimensions of the dissolved chain, which we may call $\sqrt{\overline{r^2}}$ without any qualifying subscript, are larger than $\sqrt{\overline{r_0^2}}$ by some "expansion factor" usually designated by the lower-case Greek letter alpha (α). That is,

$$\sqrt{\overline{r^2}} = \alpha \ \sqrt{\overline{r_0^2}}$$

In real solutions of synthetic polymers, α can have values as high as 5 or more. We will meet the temperature Θ and the expansion factor α again in later chapters.

THE MOLECULAR-SIZE DISTRIBUTION

You will recall that we pointed out that a single polymer chain, coiling randomly around in solution, takes up many different conformations, and therefore many different sizes, over a period of time. The average size of the chain was the important quantity to think about. Now we want to look briefly at the distribution of sizes from which this average is calculated.

Let us ask the following question, using the illustration of Figure 20: If we place one end of our chain at a known position, that is, at the origin of a set of axes labeled x, y, and z, what is the chance, w, that the other end of the chain will be found in a small box whose sides have the lengths dx, dy, and dz (where the d's indicate very small

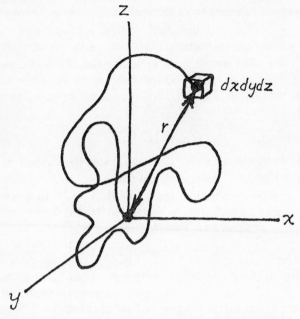

Fig. 20. This figure illustrates another question related to the random-flight calculation: What is the chance *w* of finding the two ends of a chain in two specific locations a distance *r* apart?

lengths in the *x, y,* and *z* directions) located at a distance *r* away from the origin?

The answer to this question can be written down in the form of a mathematical equation, but we need only look at a plot of this equation, Figure 21. This curve shows that there are many conformations (that is, there is a high value of the probability *w*) for which the two ends of the chain lie close together; as the ends get farther apart, the chance of finding such an arrangement gets smaller. This is proof that the fully-extended conformation of the chain, shown in Figure 3, occurs only very rarely indeed.

This distribution curve is also related to the fraction of the chain segments found at different distances from the

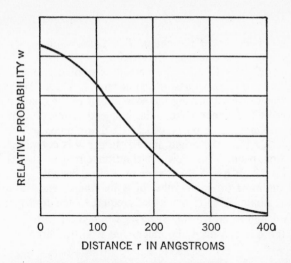

Fig. 21. This is the answer to the question in the previous caption: A plot of how the chance of finding the chain ends at two specific points separated by a distance *r* varies with *r*. The distance is calculated by the random-flight method for a polyethylene-like chain of ten thousand links.

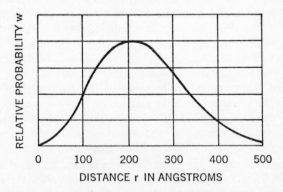

Fig. 22. If we ask instead about the total chance *w* of finding the second end of a chain anywhere as long as it is a distance *r* from the first end, this is how *w* varies with *r*. The highest point in the curve occurs at the most probable value of *r*.

center of gravity of the chain. This curve similarly drops off as one goes out from the origin.

But to get a feel for the average size of the chain, we should modify our question somewhat and ask: What is the chance, w, of finding the second end of the chain *anywhere* at a distance r from the first end? Now, the larger r is, the more little boxes of size dx dy dz there are at the distance r from the origin and the larger w is compared to the first result. The new distribution curve is shown in Figure 22. It has a maximum in w at a distance we can call the most probable value of r, the end-to-end distance of the chain. This is not exactly equal to the root-mean-square end-to-end distance $\sqrt{r^2}$, which is a little larger, but the one can easily be calculated from the other.

THE VOLUME OCCUPIED BY A CHAIN

After talking so long about the end-to-end size of a synthetic polymer chain, let us now think about the volume it occupies. This should give us an answer to the question, what size box would it take to contain all of the randomly-coiling molecule?

Because the size of the chain varies so much with time, it is possible to answer this sort of question only in statistical terms. We can say, for example, that a certain size box will contain all the chain segments a certain fraction of the time, or some fraction of the chain all of the time, but it is not possible to make firmer statements.

For the moment, let us think of the randomly-coiling chain as being spherical in shape.

Then it is possible to calculate that a sphere with a diameter 2.5 times the end-to-end distance will be big enough to contain all the chain segments on the average, while one with a diameter $5 \sqrt{r^2}$ will contain all of the chain 95 per cent of the time. It is reasonable to take this as the "diameter" of the molecule; only once in twenty times will some of the chain segments be found sticking out of this sphere.

For our polyethylene chain of two thousand carbon

atoms and the corresponding bead molecule, thinking for convenience in terms of the unperturbed end-to-end distance $\sqrt{r_0^2}$, the diameter of this sphere containing the molecule would be $5 \times 178 = 890$ A. For our bead molecule, therefore, this diameter is 890 cm or about twenty-nine feet! This is worth saying again: If our eighty-three-foot-long model were a real dissolved polymer chain, but not even expanded over its unperturbed dimensions due to interactions with a solvent, it would take a sphere almost thirty feet in diameter to contain all of the coil most of the time. That's about the size of a small house!

Now, what would be inside this sphere? Obviously, mostly solvent and very little chain. If I were to wind up my model tightly like a ball of string, it would be considerably less than a foot in diameter. In fact, the volume of all the segments of the real polyethylene chain is about fifteen thousand times less than the volume of the sphere we have been talking about!

These facts, which show impressively how much the randomly-coiling polymer chain is expanded, have an important bearing on the ways in which we measure the molecular weights and sizes of synthetic polymers, as we shall see in later chapters.

THE SHAPES OF RANDOM-COIL POLYMERS

A few pages back we said we could assume that the randomly-coiling polymer chain had a spherical shape. This is quite correct as long as we think about the average shape of the chain as it tumbles and twists about, buffeted by the small molecules around it.

This average shape is all that is really necessary to explain the behavior of the polymer molecule and the measurements we can make on it. But it is interesting to note that if we were to grab the two ends of the chain and ask what the rest of it is doing, we would find that the diameter of the chain is on the average a little greater in the direction of the line joining its ends than at right angles to this line. Thus the chain looks a bit like a football.

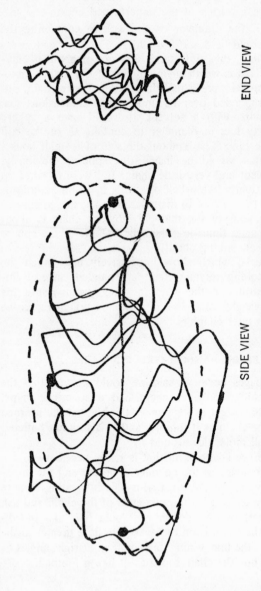

SIDE VIEW   END VIEW

Fig. 23. If we know where the middle link of the chain is, as well as the ends, a careful look shows that the average shape of the chain is more like that of a bean.

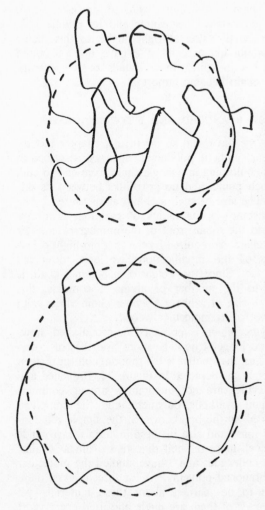

Fig. 24. For the same number of chain segments, and therefore the same molecular weight, a branched chain has a smaller size than a linear chain. It is rather silly to think in terms of the end-to-end distance, now that there are many more than two ends on the chain! Here is a case where our other measure of the size of a chain, its radius of gyration, is useful.

If we want to go still further, we can also locate the middle link of the chain, as in Figure 23. Then we would find that the chain is a bit more extended, on the average, in the direction between its center and its middle link, compared to the direction at right angles to this, being shaped something like a bean. We have not yet found any experiments in which these details of the average shape of the chain become important.

THE SIZES OF BRANCHED AND NETWORK CHAINS

Everything we have said so far in this chapter has referred to linear synthetic polymers, which we described in Chapter 2 as continuing in a single chain from end to end, with no branch points and no crosslinks between its different parts. The size of such a chain, as measured by its end-to-end distance or its radius of gyration, is always proportional to the square root of the number of links or atoms in the chain, as required by the random-flight calculation. None of the modifications we have discussed changes this fact. Since the weight of a polymer chain is proportional to the number of atoms it contains, this means that the size of a linear polymer chain varies with the square root of its molecular weight.

If the polymer chain is branched or crosslinked, however, this is no longer true. The more branches or crosslinks a chain has, the smaller is the random coil for a given molecular weight, as depicted in Figure 24. Branched and network molecules are not uncommon among commercially important synthetic polymers, and the complications introduced by the breakdown of the simple relationship between mass and size in these materials have made their study much more difficult than that of linear chains. Although my colleagues and I have studied the molecular structure of branched polyethylene for fifteen years, there is still much to be learned about these materials—yet billions of pounds of them are made and used every year!

PART II

Characterizing
Polymer Molecules

Chapter 5

SOME WAYS
OF COUNTING MOLECULES

In the preceding chapters we have developed a picture of
the molecules of a synthetic polymer—those randomly-
coiling strands for which we can use a long string of
"pop-it" beads as a model. We have talked about what
these chains are like and how they are made. We have
seen that the size of a single polymer molecule varies in
a random way with time, and obtained, by calculation, a
rough idea of how big such a chain really is.

Finally, we have seen that any real sample of polymer
contains molecules of many different weights. We have
talked briefly about some of the different kinds of average
molecular weights used to describe the complex mixtures
of molecules that make up a synthetic polymer—that is,
its molecular-weight distribution.

But we have not yet asked why it is important to measure these average molecular weights, and to find out what
these distributions are like. There is a very good reason
why these questions are important: The properties of
synthetic polymers depend on these quantities, and
change as the average molecular weights or the nature of
the distribution is varied. By making many samples with
different polymerization conditions, the polymer scientist
can prepare materials with a wide variety of molecular
weights and distributions. He can then study their properties, discovering which ones are sensitive to changes in
the various average molecular weights and the other factors that describe the structure of his samples.

Much research of this kind has been carried out in the past twenty-five years or so. The goal of these studies has not been merely to learn about polymers already made, but to learn how to go about making even better materials: stronger, tougher, more resistant to heat, weather, or cold, and generally more useful to you and me.

Here is one example of how my colleagues and I undertook this "tailoring" process to provide a new and better material that is widely used today, the acrylic* lacquers used to paint automobiles. We knew from the results of earlier research that some properties of polymers depend on the number of ends of molecular chains present. The presence of these polymer chain ends seems to create defects that spoil or disturb the structure of the polymer. For example, in a solid piece of plastic these defect-sensitive properties include strength, toughness, resistance to attack by chemicals, and resistance to cracking and surface roughening on prolonged exposure to sunlight. All these features, so important for a paint film for automobiles, improve as the number of polymer chain ends gets smaller.

Now the way to reduce the number of chain ends in a polymer is to reduce the number of molecules, and this can be done by making the remaining molecules longer. In fact, we have seen that the number-average molecular weight is a direct measure of the number of molecules, so it followed that the properties of our acrylic lacquer films would improve as their number-average molecular weight increased. Indeed this was the case, and we soon learned what level of $\bar{M}_n$ was required to get good properties in these lacquer films.

To do this, of course, we had to know how to measure $\bar{M}_n$. You may remember that we defined this quantity as the kind of average we obtain by counting up all the

* The word acrylic describes polymers with a particular group of atoms substituted for a hydrogen on every second carbon atom of the basic polyethylene chain. Depending on the nature of this side group, the family of acrylic polymers includes the glassy plastic Plexiglas and the wool-like fiber Orlon, in addition to the lacquers described here.

molecules in a polymer sample, and dividing the total mass of the sample by the number of molecules it contains. We wrote this as the formula $\bar{M}_n = W/N$ and said that we call this simple counting average the number average because it is so easily obtained from the number of molecules in the sample. Remember, too, that we measure molecular weights on a scale in which a single hydrogen atom is given the weight of 1, carbon 12, and so on, rather than in grams or pounds.

Now, how can we count molecules?

WHAT ARE THE ENDS OF THE MOLECULES LIKE?

Let us go back to the "pop-it" bead model. When I first made a model of this kind, I found that it was sometimes hard to locate the ends of the chain of beads when it was tangled up as we think real polymer molecules are. So I "tagged" the ends by adding to each a bead of a different color.

I soon realized that I was again duplicating a feature of real polymer chains. Even in the simple case of polyethylene, we saw in Chapter 1, the fact that each carbon atom requires four bonds makes the ends of the chain different from the rest of it. For example, a real polyethylene chain may have a $-CH_3$ group on one or both ends, and some kinds of linear polyethylene are known to have what the chemists call a vinyl group $-CH = CH_2$, much like those described in Chapter 2, on one end only. We saw, too, that polymers made by stepwise polymerization have such chemical groups as $-COOH$ or $-NH_2$ on the ends.

Now, if we could count these chemical groups, and knew whether they were located on one or both ends of the molecules, we could get a count of the number of molecules in our sample. This can in fact be done by chemical means.

These chemical ways of counting molecules are known as *end-group analyses* because we can relate the number of chemically countable groups to the number of molecules only if the groups are located at specific places along the chain. Practically, these places have to be the ends of the molecule—and we must restrict the use of end-group analysis to molecules that have only two ends, that is, those that are linear rather than branched.

The use of end-group analyses to count molecules and thus determine the number-average molecular weight is quite old. It was applied by Hermann Staudinger to demonstrate the long-chain nature of synthetic polymers in the years before this concept was widely accepted. At first, Staudinger was uncertain about the nature of the end groups on some of the polymers he was working with because with his relatively crude experiments he could not find *any* end groups! He later realized, however, that he just had some very long chains and, correspondingly, a small number of ends.

The same problem still bothers the polymer scientist today. Any method of counting molecules must fail when the number of molecules in a sample, large as it is, gets too small to count—that is, when the average molecular weight gets too high. Most chemical methods of end-group analysis work well only for polymers whose number-average molecular weights are below twenty-five thousand or so. Many synthetic polymers have still higher molecular weights, and other means must be sought to measure them. In addition, for many polymers we either do not know what the end groups are or cannot count them chemically. Consequently, this method does not work in all cases.

COUNTING MOLECULES BY THERMODYNAMICS

Thermodynamics is the study of the changes in heat and energy that go along with changes in the state or condition in which we find a material.

For example, if a piece of synthetic polymer is a solid chunk of plastic, all of its molecules are surrounded and tangled up with others of the same kind. When the material is dissolved, the polymer chains are surrounded by small solvent molecules, and the state of the polymer is changed. Thermodynamics helps us find out how much energy it takes to do this, how much heat is given off or absorbed in the process, and other related information.

Now let us consider what happens to the solvent in this change of state. Instead of making up the entire sample, the solvent is diluted by the presence of a number of polymer molecules. It no longer is the only material having an effect on the properties of the solution. This is quite significant, and I wish to explain further by selecting one specific property of the solution as an example.

Since the solvent molecules are small, they can easily exist in the gas or vapor state as well as in the liquid state. This is not true of polymer molecules: As the size of a molecule increases, so does its boiling point. Long before the size we call a polymer is reached, boiling temperatures get so high that the molecular chains break apart rather than go into the vapor state.

The pressure exerted by the gaseous solvent molecules, as they exist in equilibrium with—that is, interchanging freely with—their companions in the liquid, is less in the presence of the polymer molecules than it would be if only the solvent were present. We say that the "activity" of the solvent molecules is reduced by the presence of the polymer. Very crudely, one can think that the passage of solvent molecules from the liquid to the vapor is impeded by the polymer. Hence there are fewer solvent molecules in the gaseous state, decreasing the amount of pressure exerted on the wall of the container (Figure 25).

Thermodynamics tells us that this change in pressure is just proportional to the *number* of *polymer* molecules in the solution. This fact was first discovered—not for polymer solutions, but for mixtures of different kinds of small molecules—a hundred years ago by the famous French chemist François Marie Raoult. Raoult's law states that the ratio of the vapor pressure of the solvent over the solution to that over the pure solvent, at the same temperature, is a measure of the number of other molecules, besides the solvent, in the solution. Thus, if we can measure the appropriate vapor pressures, we can count molecules and hence measure the number-average molecular weight of the polymer.

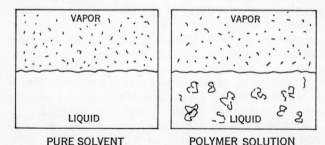

PURE SOLVENT   POLYMER SOLUTION

Fig. 25. In the presence of polymer molecules, the pressure exerted by the solvent vapor is reduced from that existing over the pure solvent at the same temperature.

Before examining how we might do this, I must say that Raoult's law does not apply to all mixtures, but only under special circumstances when one has what we call an *ideal* solution. This has an important effect for measurements with dissolved polymers, as I will describe in the next section.

There are several other properties of polymer solutions that show the same behavior as vapor-pressure lowering. They include some very familiar things. For example, the freezing point of a polymer solution is lower than that of the pure solvent. This depression of the freezing point is the same effect that is used in most of the United States every winter, when drivers add "antifreeze" to the water in the radiators of their cars, reducing the freezing point below the lowest temperature they expect to encounter during the cold weather.

Similarly, the boiling point of a polymer solution is higher than that of the pure solvent. Finally, an osmotic pressure is developed when a polymer solution and the pure solvent are placed on opposite sides of a membrane or "screen" through which the solvent molecules can pass but the polymer cannot.

These four properties that can be used to count molecules are called the *colligative properties* of solutions, the word colligative meaning to depend on the number and not the nature of the molecules. Some of the colligative properties are more suitable for use with polymer solutions than others, because of the very high molecular weights that must be dealt with, and the relatively small numbers of molecules that must be counted. This is illustrated in Table 1, which lists the magnitude of each of the colligative properties for a typical polymer solution. I have calculated these numbers for the case of a solution of one gram of the polymer polystyrene, with number-average molecular weight 20,000, dissolved in 100 cubic centimeters of a typical solvent, benzene.

Table 1 shows that the vapor-pressure lowering for this polymer solution is very small indeed, only about 1/1,000,000 of the pressure of the atmosphere. So small a difference between two pressures is almost impossibly difficult to measure, but as explained later in this chapter, we can utilize this pressure difference in a somewhat indirect way to measure polymer molecular weights.

TABLE 1

MAGNITUDE OF THE COLLIGATIVE PROPERTIES
OF A TYPICAL POLYMER SOLUTION

Property	Approximate Value
Vapor-pressure lowering	1/1,000,000 atmosphere
Freezing-point depression	1/1,000 degree Celsius
Boiling-point elevation	1/1,000 degree Celsius
Osmotic pressure	15 cm solvent

The freezing-point lowering and boiling-point elevation for this same polymer solution are each about 1/1,000 degree Celsius. This is a small temperature difference, to be sure, but it can be measured accurately using modern techniques, as we will see presently.

But the osmotic pressure exerted by the same solution is enough to support a column of the solvent some 15 cm high. This can easily be measured with high precision. If there were no other difficulties with the osmotic method, it would always be chosen for measuring the number-average molecular weight. Unfortunately, there are reasons why it is not universally applicable, so one or more of the other colligative properties must be used from time to time, despite the small size of the quantities to be measured.

THE NONIDEALITY OF POLYMER SOLUTIONS

Chemists have known for many years that most solutions or mixtures of different substances do not show the ideal behavior required if Raoult's law is to hold and the colligative properties are accurately to measure the number of molecules of dissolved material. Ideal behavior is most often found if the two substances being mixed are almost identical in size and all other properties. It is not at all surprising, therefore, that polymer solutions, where the giant long-chain molecules are so much larger than those of the solvent, never approach ideal behavior.

In fact, the great difference in size between polymer and solvent molecules required the development of a special branch of thermodynamics before the properties of polymer solutions were well understood. This thermodynamics of high polymer solutions was developed independently by Paul J. Flory and the American chemist Maurice L. Huggins in the early 1940s. We will require only one result from it to understand the conditions under which the colligative properties can be used to count polymer molecules.

The theory of Flory and Huggins shows that the behavior required by Raoult's law (and the other laws corresponding to it for the remaining colligative properties) is approached more and more closely as the concentration, or amount, of polymer in the solution is reduced. If we could measure at zero concentration of polymer, ideal behavior would be achieved. Obviously we cannot do this, for we would have only the solvent present, but we can easily estimate what the colligative properties of a polymer solution at zero concentration would be from measurements made at finite concentrations.

Let us take the measurement of the osmotic pressure as an example. The ideal-solution law for this colligative

property is that formulated around 1880 by the Dutch
scientist Jacobus H. van't Hoff. It states that the osmotic
pressure, which we can designate π (note that this is
not the numerical constant 3.1416) is proportional to
the temperature of the experiment, T, the concentration
of the solution, C, and the number of dissolved molecules. It is, therefore, inversely proportional to the
number-average molecular weight $\bar{M}_n$. The constant R
relating these quantities, called the "gas constant," is
known from other experiments. We can write the following equation describing van't Hoff's law:

$$\pi = RTC/\bar{M}_n$$

To get an idea of the numbers involved, let us assume
that the solution described in Table 1 was ideal, and
consequently van't Hoff's law was obeyed. We can therefore substitute 15 cm solvent for π. Expressing the osmotic pressure in this way and the concentration C in
grams per milliliter, the value of R is approximately 100,-
000 at room temperature. In this and all thermodynamic
equations, the temperature must be expressed on the absolute scale devised by the Scottish physical scientist Wil-
liam Thompson, Lord Kelvin. The zero point of the Kelvin scale is at the absolute zero of temperature; 0° Celsius
is 273K.*

For the convenience of round numbers, assume that
this osmotic experiment was carried out at 27° Celsius
or 300K. Then, on substituting the above numbers into
van't Hoff's law, we have

$$15 = 100,000 \times 300 \times 0.01 / \bar{M}_n$$

Solving, $\bar{M}_n = 20,000$.

The thermodynamic theory of Flory and Huggins shows
that the nonideal behavior of polymer solutions can be
taken into account by adding to van't Hoff's equation
additional terms in the square, cube and higher powers
of the concentration, C:

$$\pi = RT(A_1C + A_2C^2 + A_3C^3 + \ldots)$$

* By recent convention, the word degree and the symbol ° are
omitted when the Kelvin temperature scale is used.

This type of modification is known as a virial expansion and A_1, A_2, A_3 are called the first, second, and third virial coefficients. By comparison with van't Hoff's ideal solution equation we see that A_1, the first virial coefficient, is $1/\bar{M}_n$.

For most polymer solutions, A_3 and all the higher virial coefficients are negligibly small. Eliminating these and dividing both sides of our equation by RTC gives the following relation, which is used by the polymer scientists for determining $\bar{M}_n$ from osmotic-pressure measurements:

$$\frac{\pi}{RTC} = \frac{1}{\bar{M}_n} + A_2 \, C$$

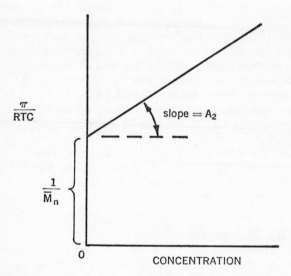

Fig. 26. The line on this graph is characteristic of the osmotic data from a polymer solution. When the quantity π/RTC, defined in the text, is plotted for different concentrations, a straight line can be drawn through the points. The intercept of this line at $C = 0$ is equal to $1/\bar{M}_n$, and the slope, labeled A_2, is a measure of the interaction forces between the polymer and the solvent.

This equation describes a straight line on a graph of π/RTC against C. The intercept of the line on the axis at $C = 0$ is $1/\bar{M}_n$, and the slope of the line is the second virial coefficient, A_2 (Figure 26). The equation tells us that if we measure the osmotic pressure π at several concentrations C of polymer, and calculate π/RTC for each set of values, we can draw the required straight line, find its intercept at $C = 0$, and thus calculate $\bar{M}_n$. A typical set of numerical values of π and C is given in Table 2, and Figure 27 shows the resulting plot. Again, I have taken R (gas constant) $= 100,000$ and T (temperature) $= 300$K.

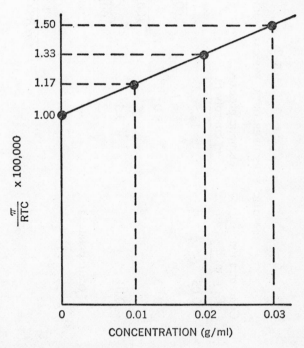

Fig. 27. This plot uses the numerical values listed in Table 2, for a polymer with $\bar{M}_n = 100,000$.

TABLE 2

OSMOTIC PRESSURES OF A TYPICAL POLYMER SOLUTION

Concentration C, g/ml	Osmotic pressure, π, cm solvent	$\dfrac{\pi}{RTC}$
0.03	13.5	$\dfrac{13.5}{100,000 \times 300 \times 0.03} = \dfrac{1.5}{100,000}$
0.02	8.0	$\dfrac{8.0}{100,000 \times 300 \times 0.02} = \dfrac{1.33}{100,000}$
0.01	3.5	$\dfrac{3.5}{100,000 \times 300 \times 0.01} = \dfrac{1.17}{100,000}$
0 (extrapolated)	—	$\dfrac{1.00}{100,000}$

$$\bar{M}_n = \frac{1}{(\pi/RTC)_{C=0}} = 100,000$$

The Flory-Huggins theory shows, in addition to what I have already said, that the second virial coefficient is a measure of the polymer-solvent interactions we described in Chapter 4. It is, in fact, often called the polymer-solvent interaction constant. When the polymer-solvent interaction forces vanish, at the special Flory temperature Θ, the second virial coefficient A_2 becomes zero. This is one way to find the theta temperature: We can make osmotic-pressure measurements at different temperatures until we find the exact temperature at which $A_2 = 0$. Then the straight line in our plot of π/RTC versus C will be parallel to the concentration axis (Figure 28). Note that if the same polymer sample is meas-

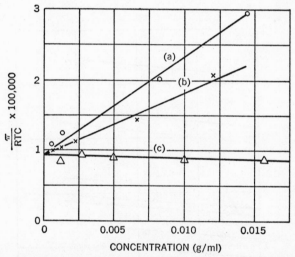

Fig. 28. Here are some osmotic-pressure data for a polymer sample, taken from experiments using three different solvents. Since the same sample was used in all three cases, the intercept of the straight lines, whose inverse is the molecular weight of the sample, is the same. The slopes are different because the polymer-solvent interaction forces differed from one solvent to another. Solvent (c) is very nearly a theta-solvent, with $A_2 = 0$. (This and Figures 29 and 30 are taken from my *Textbook of Polymer Science*, second edition, Wiley-Interscience, 1971.)

ured at several different temperatures, or in several different solvents, the lines will all have the same intercept since
$\bar{M}_n$ is always the same, but the slopes of the lines will differ, reflecting different values of A_2.

The second virial coefficient is very nearly independent of molecular weight for a given type of polymer.
Therefore, as illustrated in Figure 29, the lines representing the osmotic pressure data for several samples of
the same kind of polymer in the same solvent will all
have the same slope, but their intercepts will differ, reflecting their different molecular weights. The higher $\bar{M}_n$,
the lower π/RTC, as we have seen.

One last point: How do we know that the colligative

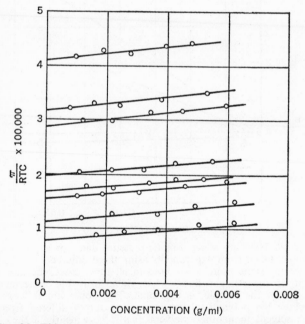

Fig. 29. This figure shows the osmotic data for several samples of the same kind of polymer, dissolved in the same solvent, but having different molecular weights.

properties measure $\bar{M}_n$ and not some other kind of molecular weight? We can show this very easily, using van't Hoff's equation. We have only to assume that each polymer molecule contributes to the osmotic pressure independent of the others, which is correct for an ideal solution. Then we can say that each molecule of kind x in the solution, with molecular weight M_x and concentration C_x, gives an osmotic pressure π_x and by van't Hoff's law,

$$\pi_x = RTC_x/M_x$$

The total osmotic pressure is just the sum of all the π_x's, and this is equal to RTC divided by some average molecular weight for all the molecules, $\bar{M}$:

$$\pi = \sum_{x=1}^{x=\infty} \pi_x = RTC/\bar{M}$$

By summing the above equation for the individual molecules, and recalling that constant quantities such as R and T can be factored out of the sum, we see that

$$\Sigma \pi_x = RT \sum_{x=1}^{x=\infty} \left(\frac{C_x}{M_x} \right)$$

Equating the two terms equaling $\Sigma \pi_x$, canceling out RT, and solving for $\bar{M}$ gives

$$\bar{M} = \frac{C}{\displaystyle\sum_{x=1}^{x=\infty} \left(\frac{C_x}{M_x} \right)}$$

Now the concentrations appearing here are just weights of material in a certain volume (say 1 ml) of solution, so we can substitute W and W_x for C and C_x. Remember also that $W_x = M_x N_x$ as we showed in Chapter 3. Then we see that

$$\bar{M} = \frac{W}{\sum\limits_{x=1}^{x=\infty} \left(\dfrac{W_x}{M_x}\right)} = \frac{W}{\sum\limits_{x=1}^{x=\infty} N_x} = \frac{W}{N} = \bar{M}_n$$

since ΣN_x is just the total number of molecules, N. Since $\bar{M}$ has the same definition, W/N, as $\bar{M}_n$, the osmotic-pressure experiment must in fact measure the number-average molecular weight. The same conclusion applies to the other colligative properties as well.

MEMBRANE OSMOMETRY

Now I wish to describe the osmotic experiment in a little more detail. Figure 30 shows the principle involved. The instrument in which the measurement is carried out, called an *osmometer,* has two compartments that are closed except for small-diameter glass tubes attached to their tops. The compartments are separated by a *semi-*

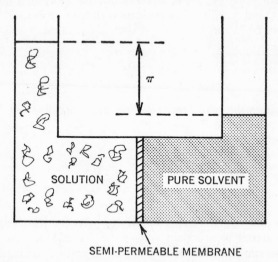

SEMI-PERMEABLE MEMBRANE

Fig. 30. An illustration of the principle of operation of a simple membrane osmometer, as described in the text.

permeable membrane, a film that allows the small solvent molecules to pass freely from one compartment to the other, but does not let the much larger polymer molecules go through. Usually this film is made of a plastic that itself does not dissolve in the solvent being used. Quite often the film is cellophane.

In the osmotic experiment, pure solvent is placed in one compartment and polymer solution in the other. As we have seen, the solvent in the two compartments is not in the same state, its activity being lower in the presence of the polymer molecules. Thermodynamics predicts that solvent molecules will flow through the membrane into the polymer solution in this case, making it more dilute and bringing its solvent molecules closer to the state of those in the pure solvent.

In the closed compartments of the osmometer, the passage of solvent through the membrane raises the liquid level in the small capillary tube on the solution side, and lowers it on the solvent side. This gives rise to a difference in pressure of the liquid on the two sides, measured by the pressure exerted by the column of solution whose length is the difference in height in the two capillary tubes. This pressure, of course, makes some of the solvent molecules flow back through the membrane toward the solvent side, since a liquid always seeks to have the same level. Thus there is a flow of solvent in each direction. When the pressure of the liquid column is just equal to the osmotic pressure, the two flows are equal and opposite, and the difference in liquid levels remains constant. This is what we measure.

Actual osmometers are built very much like the sketch of Figure 30. Two of the types used for many years are shown in the photographs of Plates 3 and 4. You can easily identify the various parts of them that we have discussed.

One drawback to these relatively simple osmometers is that it takes a long time for enough solvent to pass through the semipermeable membrane to fill the volume of the capillary tube to the required height. One has to wait from one to perhaps fifteen hours for the osmometer to come to equilibrium, so that the measurements are slow and tedious. Within the past few years, a new type of osmometer has overcome this problem by using a sensitive device to detect the first tiny amount of solvent flow and quickly apply the necessary pressure of the liquid column in order to bring the flow to a halt. These

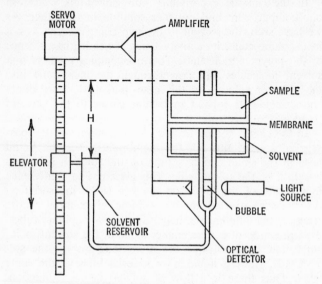

Fig. 31. The principle of operation of one of the recently developed high-speed automatic osmometers. The membrane in this instrument is supported horizontally, with the polymer solution in an open cell above and the solvent below. A small bubble of air is trapped in a glass capillary tube connected to the solvent compartment. As solvent moves through the membrane, this bubble moves also. Its position is detected by a phototube and lamp as shown. When the bubble moves, the change in the amount of light hitting the phototube causes an electrical signal which, after amplification, drives a motor controlling the level of a cup of solvent. The instrument is adjusted so that the solvent cup moves in the right direction to supply the difference in liquid level—the osmotic pressure—just sufficient to prevent the air bubble from moving. All this takes place in about the time it has taken you to read this paragraph. The instrument itself is shown in Plate 5. (Courtesy of Hewlett-Packard Corp.)

osmometers come to equilibrium in five to ten minutes, speeding up the measurements about a hundredfold. One of them is described in Figure 31, and Plate 5.

The major problem of membrane osmometry—and it is a severe one—lies in the less-than-perfect nature of the semipermeable membranes we have available. None of them is perfectly semipermeable. All of them let some of the smaller polymer molecules pass through, as well as the solvent. When this happens, the polymer molecules that have gone through the membrane do not contribute to the osmotic pressure any longer. The pressure that is measured is too small; the number of molecules counted is too small, and the molecular weight that is calculated is too large. The error can be very serious: In some of the studies of polyethylene that my colleagues and I carried out a few years ago, the osmotic results were too high by as much as a factor of three!

Consequently, we now realize that the osmotic method can only be applied to polymers of rather high molecular weight, which do not contain any molecules small enough to pass through the membranes. Just how high depends on the exact nature of the sample and the membranes used, and is difficult to predict. Perhaps 25,000 is a reasonable lower limit of molecular weight that can be measured by osmometry with today's membrane materials. There are many samples of interest to the polymer scientist whose molecular weight is below this limit; to measure these materials, the other colligative methods described in the next section must be used. For molecular weights higher than 25,000, membrane osmometry is satisfactory up to the point where the osmotic pressure gets too small to measure; this occurs around a molecular weight of 1,000,000, and there are very few polymers indeed with number-average molecular weight this high.

THE OTHER COLLIGATIVE PROPERTIES

Earlier we listed the four colligative properties that can be used to count molecules and thus measure the number-average molecular weight: vapor-pressure lowering, boiling-point elevation, freezing-point lowering, and the osmotic pressure. We then saw that, despite the larger size of the osmotic pressure, making it easier to measure than the other colligative properties, membrane osmometry is not applicable to all polymers because of our inability to find or make perfect semipermeable membranes. Now we must re-examine the possibility of making use of one or more of the remaining colligative properties to measure $\bar{M}_n$ in the region below, say, 25,000, where the osmotic method cannot be used.

It is fitting to consider the three remaining colligative properties at the same time, because they have much in common. For example, they all involve the measurement of small temperature differences. This is obvious for the case of *ebulliometry,* or measurement of the boiling-point elevation, and for *cryoscopy,* the measurement of the freezing-point depression, but a little explanation is needed to relate vapor-pressure lowering to a temperature measurement.

We saw that the vapor-pressure lowering in a polymer solution is very small. Moreover, it would take a very long time—days or even weeks—to establish equilibrium between a polymer solution and the pure solvent if the solvent flow were to be through the vapor, as required by this method, rather than through a semipermeable membrane, as in membrane osmometry. During all this time, the temperature of the apparatus would have to be held within very close limits, about 1/1,000,000 degree, because the vapor pressures of liquids depend very strongly on temperature. This is just too difficult for us to do at this stage of our scientific knowledge.

We can get around these difficulties by using the following trick: We place two small droplets of liquid—one, the pure solvent, and the other, a polymer solution—on two of the modern sensitive temperature-measuring devices called *thermistors,* in an arrangement sketched in Figure 32. The two drops are held in a closed chamber containing the vapor of the solvent. We have seen already that there is a continuous movement of solvent molecules back and forth from the liquid to the vapor, and this

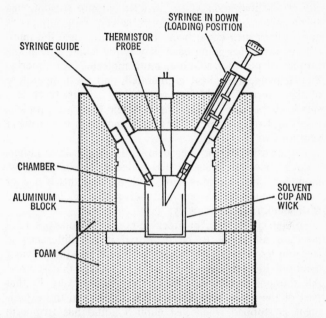

Fig. 32. The arrangement of the thermistor temperature sensors and liquid drops in the instrument called the "vaporphase osmometer." Hypodermic syringes are used to place the drops of liquid on the thermistors. The text explains how this instrument operates, and a photograph of it is shown in Plate 6. (Courtesy of Hewlett-Packard Corp.)

takes place at both droplets of liquid. But, as we also saw, the presence of the polymer acts in such a way as to make the movement of solvent molecules out of the solution droplet appear to be impeded. As a result, more solvent molecules enter the solution drop than leave it. At the droplet of pure solvent, there is no impeding effect, and the flows of solvent into and out of this drop exactly balance.

Now, the change of state of a liquid to its vapor requires heat, as you know very well from the simple act of boiling water. When the reverse change, from vapor to liquid, takes place, this heat (called the heat of *vapori-*

zation) is liberated. At the droplet of pure solvent, just as much heat is used to vaporize solvent molecules as is given off as they come back to the liquid, since the number of molecules going each way is the same. But at the droplet of polymer solution, more molecules are entering than leaving, more heat is liberated, and the temperature of this drop of liquid increases slightly. Thus there is a small temperature difference between the two droplets, resulting from the vapor-pressure lowering in the polymer solution.

An instrument for measuring this temperature difference is shown in Plate 6. It is called a "vapor-phase osmometer," but you may agree with me that this is a poor name because of the possibility of confusing the method with membrane osmometry.

In the cryoscopic, or freezing-point method, the temperature difference to be measured is the difference in freezing temperatures of the pure solvent and the polymer solution. In each case, it is the pure solvent that freezes: All the polymer molecules in the solution stay in that part of the liquid that has not yet frozen, and the experiment is stopped when just enough liquid has frozen to allow measurement of the temperature at which this takes place. But in the polymer solution, the temperature has to be lowered just a bit farther before freezing starts, due to the impeding presence of the polymer molecules.

The situation is similar in the ebulliometric or boiling-point experiment, where the polymer solution boils at a slightly higher temperature than the pure solvent. As I write this, there are no commercially available instruments for either cryoscopic or ebulliometric measurements, and these two methods are not widely used.

The solid-state electronic devices known as thermistors are used as temperature sensors in each of the colligative methods discussed in this section. They work because their electrical resistance depends markedly on the temperature. It is not difficult to measure this resistance accurately; the student reader may have had the opportunity to do this sort of experiment in his physics laboratory. What one would measure in any one of the three colliga-

PLATE 7. Inside a research-model light-scattering photometer, the phototube (seen at the right) rotates on a movable arm pivoted about the center of the cell compartment. The cell itself is seen in Plate 8; what you see here is its thermostatted compartment.

PLATE 8. The cell for the light-scattering instrument shown in Plate 7 consists of a precisely made cylinder of glass, with an entrance tube to the left for the main light beam to enter through a plane window. After the beam has passed through the scattering liquid, it is caught and absorbed in a black glass "light trap" at the right side of the cell.

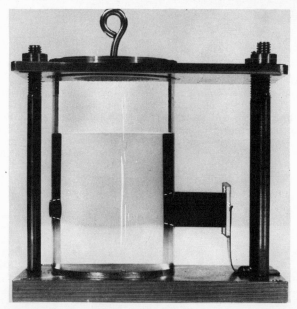

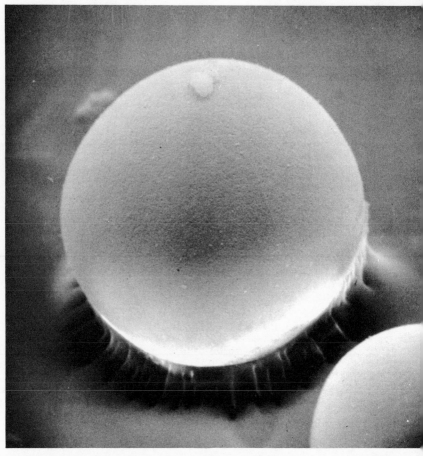

PLATE 9. This photograph shows a bead of the porous but highly crosslinked polystyrene "gel" used as a "molecular sieve" in the fractionation technique called gel permeation chromatography. It is shown here in a photograph made with a scanning electron microscope, a new technique that gives unusually detailed, almost three-dimensional-appearing photographs at very high magnification, here at about 500 times. (Courtesy of R. W. Godwin and the Celanese Fibers Co.)

PLATE 10. Here is one of the polystyrene gel beads, like that in Plate 9, that has been broken apart before examination. You can see the very uniform porous internal structure of the gel. (Courtesy of R. W. Godwin and the Celanese Fibers Co.)

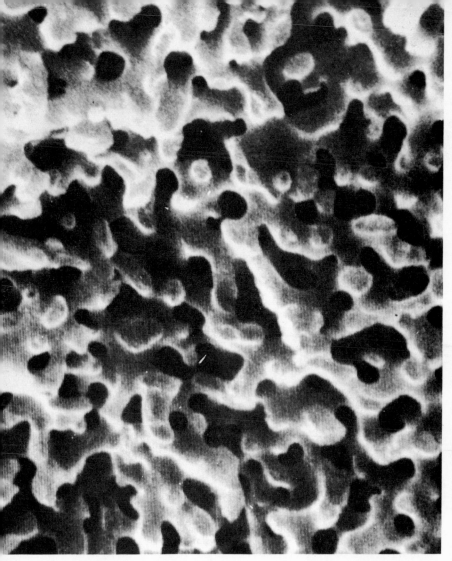

PLATE 11. At higher magnification (about 30,000 times) in a conventional electron microscope photograph, the porous internal structure of the gel permeation beads is big enough to see in detail. A typical polymer molecule would be about 1/16 inch across in its random coil, at this magnification. (Courtesy of J. C. Moore and the Dow Chemical Co.)

tive experiments I have described is the thermistor resistance, r, for the experiment with pure solvent and again for that with the polymer solution. The difference between these two electrical resistances we can call Δr, using the Greek capital delta, Δ, to indicate a difference.

Now the equations relating the colligative properties to $\bar{M}_n$ have the same form as those for the osmotic pressure, so we can write, in analogy to the equation we used before,

$$\frac{\Delta r}{C} = K\left(\frac{1}{\bar{M}_n} + A_2 C\right)$$

where K is a numerical constant that relates electrical resistance to temperature for the particular thermistor being used, and contains other terms such as the gas constant and the temperature. We know most of the numbers that are a part of K, but it is something of a nuisance to do the necessary experiments relating r to T. Instead, it is common practice to use a low-molecular-weight chemical substance, with accurately known molecular weight, as a calibration standard. Among many suitable substances are some of the paraffin family we described in Chapter 1, including octacosane, $CH_3(CH_2)_{26}CH_3$, whose molecular weight is 395, and triacontane, $CH_3(CH_2)_{28}CH_3$, with $M = 423$.

In practice, then, one of these substances is measured at several concentrations, giving values of Δr and C where $\bar{M}_n$ is known. This allows us to find the value of K. We then use this value of K in experiments with polymer solutions, and values of $\bar{M}_n$ for the polymer can be found.

The methods I have described work best for polymers of relatively low molecular weight, where the temperature differences are relatively large. With our present-day instruments, this covers the range up to about $\bar{M}_n = 25,000$ before the uncertainty in $\bar{M}_n$ becomes too great. Fortunately, this is about the point at which the membrane osmotic method becomes useful, so that with one or the other method we can count molecules and determine $\bar{M}_n$ for any polymer sample of interest.

Chapter 6

MEASURING THE MASS
OF BIG MOLECULES

At this point we know that every sample of a synthetic polymer consists of a complex mixture of large and small long-chain molecules. Because of the variety of their sizes and masses, we must always think about the properties of polymer molecules in terms of averages—that is, in a statistical way. We have learned how to measure one average quantity of some importance, the number-average molecular weight. We have seen briefly, and later on we will learn more about, how the physical properties of rubbers, plastics, and fibers depend on $\bar{M}_n$ and other quantities that describe the structure of polymer molecules.

But the number-average molecular weight results from a counting process to which every molecule contributes in the same way regardless of its mass. As molecular weight increases, it takes fewer molecules to make up a given mass of material, so that the bigger a molecule, the less it contributes to $\bar{M}_n$. This fact seems strange in comparison to the importance we have been placing on the long-chain nature of synthetic polymers. Aren't there other average properties that emphasize, rather than ignore, the contribution of the bigger molecules?

There are, indeed, and they are the subject of this and the next chapter. But let's consider for a moment just why the polymer scientist should be concerned with such properties that describe the contribution of the biggest molecules to the molecular-weight distribution. Again, the problem of producing satisfactory acrylic automotive lacquers provides an example.

These lacquers are applied, as solutions of the polymer in volatile solvents, to the auto parts by spraying with a paint spray gun. We found that if there were too many very long, high-molecular-weight polymer chains in the sample, the lacquer solutions would not spray properly. Instead of atomizing into fine droplets that gave the desired cloud of spray, the solutions formed long, stringy filaments that reminded us of cobwebs. You can imagine what sticky messes these led to, instead of the smooth coating that results when the particles of a properly prepared lacquer are sprayed on the metal parts. A little investigation showed that the cobwebbing tendency did not correlate with measured values of the number-average molecular weight. A new measure was needed, accounting directly for the contribution of the longest polymer chains. Clearly, whatever this new measure was, it could not get too high in a sprayable lacquer.

But what kind of a property do we need in order to place the proper emphasis on the masses of the bigger molecules? Should the thing that we measure be proportional to the mass of each molecule, so that every polymer chain in a mixture contributes to the average property in exact proportion to its molecular weight?

Let's see what would happen if this were true. Suppose we call the thing we are going to measure Q. Then when we say that Q is proportional to molecular weight, it means that $Q = kM$, where k is a constant. If this is true for the xth kind of molecule, and there are N_x of that kind in our mixture, then the total contribution to Q coming from the xth kind of molecule will be $N_x k M_x$, and when we sum this up over all kinds of molecules, we find that

$$Q = \sum_{x=1}^{x=\infty} N_x k M_x = k \ \Sigma \ N_x M_x$$

But we have seen $\Sigma N_x M_x$ before, in Chapter 3. It is just the weight of the sample, W. Thus, the measurement of any quantity Q that is proportional to molecular weight gives no information *about* molecular weight, but only the mass of the whole sample. We have to look farther to find something that will give proper emphasis to the big molecules, and we will find it later in this chapter.

THE INTERACTION OF LIGHT WITH MATTER

Let us turn now to consider a very common occurrence —one, in fact, that we can't ignore because it is all around us: the thing that happens whenever a beam of light hits any kind of atom.

You have probably learned in physics that light sometimes acts like a wave, sometimes like a particle. Right now we will consider light acting like a wave. What happens when one of these waves of light passes by a molecule, much like a little wavelet in the ocean passing by a floating cork? The cork bobs up and down in response to the wave, and we can think in a similar way of the electrons and nuclei in the molecule moving a little bit in response to the light wave. Whenever electrically charged particles like electrons and nuclei move back and forth regularly, they create light.

So, the interaction of light with matter always creates light. We call this process *scattering*. Since neither light nor anything else ever gets created out of nothing, some of the light in the original beam disappears in the process, and we say that whenever light interacts with matter, some of it is scattered.

The word scattering makes it sound as if the new light were moving in all different directions, and this is indeed the case. It also tells us how the scattered light differs from the original beam, which was moving in a fixed direction. In scattering, the direction of motion of some of the light is changed, but the wavelength or color of the light is not changed. This makes the scattering process different from many other ways in which light and matter interact, such as absorption, fluorescence, and luminescence.

If light scattering is so common, we must be able to

see it all around us, and so we do. The tiny amount of light scattered by the molecules of air accounts for the blue color of the sky. Scattered light from raindrops makes the rainbow. All white substances, including smokes, clouds, white paints, even the cloth of your shirt or blouse, appear white because of large amounts of light scattering.

Some famous people have been interested in light scattering. In 1873, Lord Rayleigh, who first carried out the random-flight calculation we discussed in Chapter 4, studied the scattering of light by air. He showed, among other things, that the amount of scattered light was inversely proportional to the fourth power of the wavelength of the light. That is, more light of shorter wavelengths, from the blue end of the spectrum, is scattered than is red light of longer wavelength. That is why the sky is blue. And, at sunset, when we look toward the west and see the rays of light that are left after the blue has been removed by scattering, the sun and sky look red.

Much later, around 1912, Albert Einstein (a remarkably versatile scientist who is so well known for his theory of relativity that we seldom hear of his other accomplishments) calculated and explained the scattering of light by pure liquids. Now, since liquids are more dense than air and therefore contain many more molecules in a given volume, we might expect that they would scatter much more light. But, in fact, Einstein showed that liquids scatter fifty to a hundred times less light than we might expect. This results from the optical phenomenon called destructive interference. As Figure 33 shows, light waves scattered by different molecules, so placed that the peak of one light wave meets the trough of another, cancel each other out, so to speak. This is what happens in liquids, whose structure is not completely random. Einstein showed that, if the liquid had exactly the same density at every point, no light at all would be scattered, all being destroyed by interference. It is only because real liquids vary slightly in density from place to place that they scatter small amounts of light at all.

What can we say about the relation between light scat-

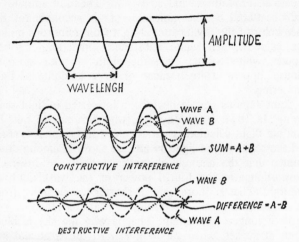

Fig. 33. When two light waves, from the same source and going in the same direction, have the same phase (that is, meet peak with peak and trough with trough), they are said to undergo constructive interference. If, on the other hand, they have opposite phases (the trough of one coincides with the peak of the other), they interfere destructively. If they have the same wavelength (distance along the wave from one peak to the next), the new wave has an amplitude (distance across the wave from peak to trough) equal to the sum of the two original amplitudes in the case of constructive interference, and to their difference in destructive interference.

tering and molecular weight? Physics tells us that the amount of light scattered, measured by the amplitude (Figure 33) or height between crest and trough of the scattered light wave, is just proportional to the total mass of all the atoms in the molecule doing the scattering. This looks like a dead end: If the amplitude of the scattered light is proportional to the mass of the scattering object, it is like the quantity Q discussed earlier in this chapter, and will tell us nothing about molecular weight. Quite true, but there is another fortunate law of physics that tells us that we can never observe the amplitude of a light wave: What we see and can measure is the intensity of the light, which is the square of the amplitude.

Thus when we measure light scattering, the quantity we observe is proportional to the *square* of the molecular weight. Big molecules really contribute to this phenomenon by amounts proportional to the squares of their masses. We shall see in the next section what kind of information about molecular weight this experiment gives.

LIGHT SCATTERING FROM POLYMER SOLUTIONS

This section is one of personal reminiscence for me, because it was my privilege to study under another truly great physicist, Peter J. W. Debye, at the time he was developing a theory for the light scattering from polymer solutions. Debye, born in Holland, was then professor of chemistry at Cornell University (another indication of the closeness of chemistry and physics), where he had come in 1939 in flight from Nazi Germany. I was, at that time, a very inexperienced graduate student. World War II had just begun, the supply of natural rubber for automobile and truck tires had been cut off by the Japanese invasion of the Far East, and the programs of the U. S. Government to produce synthetic rubbers had begun. It was Debye's task to devise and use new techniques to study the processes by which these synthetic polymers were made. This assignment led him to develop the theory of light scattering from polymer solutions.

Before looking at the results of Debye's studies, we must define exactly what we mean by the intensity of light scattering. Let us start as in Figure 34, with a beam of light with intensity I_0 passing through a cell or container holding the polymer solution to be studied. Then we can talk about either the amount of light scattered in a certain direction, or the whole amount of light removed from the beam by scattering.

Lord Rayleigh liked to think in terms of the light scattered in a given direction. Suppose we look at the scattered light coming out at an angle θ to the direction in which the main light beam is traveling. Let us call its intensity i_θ, the subscript θ being used to remind us that what we see may depend on the direction from which we

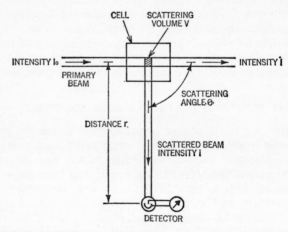

Fig. 34. If a beam of light of intensity I_0 passes through a light-scattering cell, a smaller amount of light I will emerge, because some has been scattered. At any angle θ, we can call the amount scattered i_θ. The text describes how Lord Rayleigh derived the Rayleigh ratio, R_θ, from i_θ and the other quantities shown in the figure. The difference between I_0 and I can be found by summing up i_θ for all different values of θ and for all angles around a line pointing in the direction the light is traveling.

look. We know also that the light coming from a small source—such as a molecule scattering light—spreads out as it goes, so that its intensity at any distance r from the source drops as the inverse of the square of r, following what is known as the inverse-square law. Thus, i_θ varies as $1/r^2$, which means that $i_\theta r^2$ is independent of the distance r between the light-scattering cell and the observer. The scattered intensity must also be proportional to the intensity of the incident beam, I_0, and to the volume, V, from which scattered light is coming. Lord Rayleigh was aware of all these dependences, and defined the quantity

$$R_\theta = \frac{i_\theta r^2}{I_0 V}$$

called the *Rayleigh ratio,* which describes the fraction of the incident light scattered in the direction defined by the angle θ. R_θ is therefore a quantity that ought to tell us something about polymer molecular weights.

In developing his theory of light scattering from a polymer solution, Debye showed that it is tiny fluctuations in the nature of the solution that lead to light scattering. Debye recognized that for polymer solutions the fluctuations that are important are variations in concentration, or amount of polymer in a minute volume of the solution. The fluctuations result from the random motions of the big molecules as they are buffeted about by collisions with their small solvent neighbors. The bigger these fluctuations, the more light is scattered. The result of Debye's theory is that the amount of scattering—that is, the Rayleigh ratio—is proportional to both the concentration C of the polymer solution and the molecular weight M of the polymer. We can write what is known as the Debye equation for light scattering as

$$R_\theta = KCM$$

where K is a constant describing the optical properties of the polymer solution. It lumps together such information as the wavelength of the light (appearing as the inverse fourth power, as Lord Rayleigh found), the refractive indexes of the polymer and the solvent, and numerical constants.

I have written the Debye equation in a very simple form, and now we must consider some corrections to it. I shall ignore one or two that depend only on the way the experiments are done, and add nothing essential.

But we have seen before, in talking in Chapter 5 about the measurement of number-average molecular weights by the colligative properties, that the nonideal behavior of polymer solutions cannot be ignored. Debye showed that the light-scattering equation can be written

$$K\frac{C}{R_\theta} = \frac{1}{M} + 2\,A_2 C$$

when this is taken into account. Here A_2 is the same second virial coefficient defined in Chapter 5, measuring the interaction forces between polymer and solvent. The simpler form of the Debye equation that I wrote earlier is correct in the limit of very small concentrations.

Before presenting one last important correction to the Debye equation, I would like to show you what kind of molecular-weight information the measurement of R_θ gives. One of the conditions of Debye's theory is that each polymer molecule scatters light independently, without any disturbance by its neighbors. The molecules of the xth kind, having molecular weight M_x and being present in concentration C_x, will scatter an amount of light measured by R_x (where I have omitted the subscript θ to avoid carrying double subscripts). By the Debye equation, in the ideal-solution limit,

$$R_x = KC_xM_x$$

Now the total amount of light scattered by all the molecules is obtained by summing up R_x for all the different kinds of molecules—that is, for all values of x:

$$R_\theta = \sum_{x=1}^{x=\infty} R_x = K \sum_{x=1}^{x=\infty} C_x \, M_x$$

Now let us consider the polymer solution as a whole. It acts as if the amount of light R_θ were scattered by polymer molecules with an average molecular weight $\bar{M}$, present in concentration C, where

$$C = \sum_{x=1}^{x=\infty} C_x$$

Thus,

$$R_\theta = KC\bar{M}$$

But we just saw another way of writing R_θ, and we can set the two equal:

$$R_\theta = KC\bar{M} = K \sum_{x=1}^{x=\infty} C_x M_x$$

Now we can solve the right-hand two terms for $\bar{M}$, canceling out K in the process, to define the particular kind of average molecular weight the light-scattering experiment gives. Doing this and replacing C by its equivalent ΣC_x, we obtain

$$\bar{M}_w = \frac{\sum_{x=1}^{x=\infty} C_x M_x}{\sum_{x=1}^{x=\infty} C_x}$$

I have added the subscript w to $\bar{M}$ because we call this kind of average the *weight-average molecular weight,* for the following reason.

Remember that concentration simply means the weight of material in a given volume of solution. That is, C_x is proportional to W_x. Since it occurs in both the numerator and the denominator of the equation for $\bar{M}_w$, we can replace C with W; the constant of proportionality between the two will cancel. We can write, therefore,

$$\bar{M}_w = \frac{\sum_{x=1}^{x=\infty} W_x M_x}{\sum_{x=1}^{x=\infty} W_x}$$

This looks just like the equation in Chapter 3 for the number-average molecular weight

$$\bar{M}_n = \frac{\displaystyle\sum_{x=1}^{x=\infty} N_x M_x}{\displaystyle\sum_{x=1}^{x=\infty} N_x}$$

except that N has everywhere been replaced by W. This is our justification for using the subscript w and calling this the weight-average molecular weight.

Finally, remembering that $W = NM$, we can write

$$\bar{M}_w = \frac{\displaystyle\sum_{x=1}^{x=\infty} N_x M_x^2}{\displaystyle\sum_{x=1}^{x=\infty} N_x M_x}$$

This shows how the squares of the molecular weights of the polymer molecules come in, and why the light-scattering experiment and the weight-average molecular weight truly emphasize the presence of the biggest molecules. Look again in Chapter 3 to see how these two kinds of average molecular weights are related.

THE ANGULAR DEPENDENCE
OF LIGHT SCATTERING

As I have written it, Professor Debye's equation for molecular-weight measurement by light scattering is still incomplete in one important respect. It fails to account for what one sees experimentally: The intensity of scattered light changes with the angle, θ, from which it is observed. Debye was of course aware of this, for it results from a well-known phenomenon in optics, the destructive interference mentioned before. Thinking about light scattering from a single large particle, such as a polymer molecule, we can say that interference occurs whenever the particle

is large enough to be comparable in size to the wavelength of the light.

What happens is shown in Figure 35. Unless the size

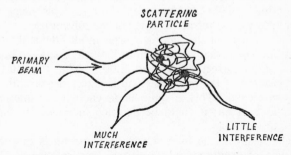

Fig. 35. If the polymer molecule is comparable in size to the
wavelength of the light, destructive interference arises from
the difference in phase between light scattered from different
parts of the molecule. Thus, the observed intensity of scattering decreases as the angle θ, and hence the phase difference,
increases.

of the particle—not its mass; this interference has nothing
to do with mass—is quite small compared to the wavelength, the scattered light coming from different parts of
the molecule will have different phases. That is, a crest of
the original light wave will be passing through one part of
the molecule, and causing scattering, at the same time that
a trough of the same light wave will be causing scattering
from another part of the same polymer molecule. What
we call *phase* is just position along the original wave:
Trough and crest are said to have different phases. The
phase of the original wave is reproduced in the scattered
waves. Thus, if the molecule is big enough, the scattered
waves from different parts of it will have different phases
and will interfere among themselves.

Are polymer molecules really big enough to exhibit this
interference? We saw in Chapter 4 that the unperturbed
end-to-end distance of our model polyethylene chain of
two thousand carbon atoms—really a rather small polymer
molecule—was about 180 A. Light-scattering experiments

with polyethylene are often performed in solvents where the actual end-to-end distance (Chapter 4) is at least twice as large, say 400 A for our example.

The wavelength in air of the kind of light used for light-scattering experiments is about 4360 A. This must be corrected for the refractive index of the solvent used, since the wavelength of the light is shorter in all liquids than it is in air. The actual wavelength of the light doing the scattering, after correction, is about 2800 A. Thus the end-to-end distance of the polymer chain is about one-seventh of the wavelength. This is quite large enough for interference to be seen; it could be detected in molecules only one-third this big.

The result of the interference phenomenon is that the amount of scattered light observed gets smaller as the angle of observation, θ, increases. The amount of this dropoff gets bigger as the size of the polymer molecule increases; this is shown in Figure 36.

We could write down an equation for the curves of Figure 36, relating the intensity of light scattering to the angle θ and to the ratio of the particle size to the wavelength of the light. This mathematical relation is called $P(\theta)$, and it appears in the Debye equation like this:

$$\frac{KC}{R_\theta} = \frac{1}{\bar{M}_w P(\theta)} + 2 A_2 C$$

This is the actual equation used by polymer scientists performing the light-scattering experiment.

MEASURING LIGHT SCATTERING

But we have not yet seen how the light-scattering measurement is made. The apparatus used is rather simple in principle, but the experiment requires careful work because the amount of light scattered by polymer solutions is quite small.

As Plates 7 and 8 show, the essential parts of a light-scattering instrument are a source of light, a cell to hold the polymer solution, and a receiver or detector to view and measure the scattered light.

In almost all the instruments I know about, the light source is a mercury-arc lamp, of the kind once widely used for lighting factories and large outdoor areas. Some modern instruments use lasers as sources, but these are not yet common. The mercury arc and the laser have the ad-

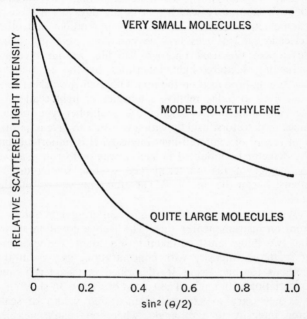

Fig. 36. This plot shows how the scattered intensity described in Figure 35 varies with the angle θ (here the haversine of θ, $\sin^2(\theta/2)$, is the appropriate function to plot), for scattering molecules of various sizes. For very small particles, there is no dependence of scattered intensity on angle; for our model polyethylene of $M = 28,000$ and end-to-end distance 400 A, the angular dependence is appreciable; and for larger-size molecules it can become quite big. These curves do not show the relative intensity levels as a function of molecular weight, since $P(\theta)$ is made to approach 1 at $\theta = 0$. Ordinarily, one expects larger sizes to go with higher molecular weights; in this case, the scattered intensities themselves would be higher at all angles for the higher-molecular-weight sample.

vantage that it is easy to get a strong beam of light of just one wavelength from them.

The cell to hold the polymer solution is made of glass. It must be carefully made, and is as fine an example of high-quality optical work as the lens on a very good camera.

Our original work on light scattering in Professor Debye's laboratory was begun in the days when modern photoelectric detectors of light, the phototubes and other "electric eye" devices now so common, were just being developed. We used photographic film as our receiver, estimating scattered-light intensities by the amount of blackening produced on the film. Other early workers used their eyes to judge relative intensities of light scattering. But all modern instruments use multiplier-type photo-tubes as detectors, usually with a recorder to give a perma-nent record of scattered-light intensity. It is important that the detector be mounted in such a way as to rotate about the center of the scattering cell so that scattered-light intensity can be measured at different values of the angle θ.

What does one do with the light-scattering data obtained from an instrument like this? The Debye equation shows that two things must be taken into account: the variation of scattered intensity with concentration, just as in the methods for measuring $\bar{M}_n$ described in Chapter 5, and its variation with angle. The curves of Figure 36 show that it is necessary to extrapolate measured values of scat-tered intensity to zero angle, where one can't measure directly because the initial light beam goes in that direc-tion but where the interference effect disappears and $P(\theta) = 1$.

The most widely used way of making these two extra-polations was devised by Bruno H. Zimm and is called the Zimm-plot method. The steps in the process of form-ing the Zimm plot are shown in Figure 37.

First, scattered intensities, as directly measured, are converted into values of the Rayleigh ratio, R_θ. This re-quires measurement of some material whose Rayleigh ratio is already known. Several of these are available; one

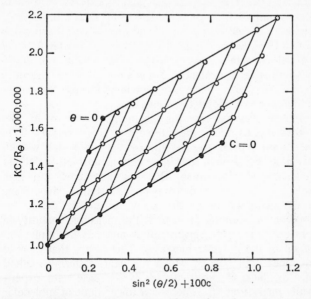

Fig. 37. This is a Zimm plot illustrating the treatment of light-scattering data. The value of KC/R_θ at which the curves extrapolate to the left-hand side of the graph, where $C = 0$ and $\theta = 0$, is $1/\bar{M}_w$. For this sample of polystyrene, $\bar{M}_w = 1,000,000$. The slopes of the curves labeled $C = 0$ and $\theta = 0$ give, as described in the text, the end-to-end distance of the sample (1000 A) and the second virial coefficient, respectively. The factor 100 in $\sin^2(\theta/2) + 100\ C$ is an arbitrary scaling factor selected to give a well-spaced plot. (Adapted from my *Textbook of Polymer Science,* second edition, Wiley-Interscience, 1971.)

commonly used substance is the low-molecular-weight liquid benzene. Measuring this material gives a calibration factor relating i_θ and R_θ, which can be used for all polymer solutions studied. Next, the values of R_θ found, at each angle θ, for the pure solvent in which the polymer is to be dissolved, are subtracted from all R_θ's measured on the polymer solutions. This leaves only the scattering due to the polymer itself, which is what we are interested in.

The quantity KC/R_θ is then calculated for each concentration and each angle of observation. One plots KC/R_θ against C for each value of θ and extrapolates each curve to $C = 0$, as we saw done for π/RTC in Chapter 5. Then the values obtained at $C = 0$ are extrapolated to $\theta = 0$ by plotting them against θ. Zimm's contribution, shown in Figure 37, was to make one plot in which the two extrapolations are made at the same time.

Just as was the case for the measurements of $\bar{M}_n$ described in Chapter 5, the intercept at $C = 0$ and $\theta = 0$, in the Zimm plot is the inverse of the molecular weight, this time $\bar{M}_w$. Again, low intercepts mean high molecular weights, and vice versa. But low intercepts and high molecular weights result from high scattering, since R_θ is in the denominator of the Debye equation. Unlike the situation in counting molecules, the measured quantity in light scattering gets bigger, not smaller, as the molecular weight of the polymer increases. This means that there is no upper limit beyond which the light-scattering method fails for lack of sensitivity, as is the case with experiments measuring $\bar{M}_n$. There is a lower limit of molecular weight, below which too little light is scattered to give good results, but this is below the level of polymer molecular weights in most cases.

As in the measurements of $\bar{M}_n$, the second virial coefficient is measured by the concentration dependence of the light-scattering data. The line marked $\theta = 0$ on Figure 37 has a slope of $2 A_2$, as required by the Debye equation. The Zimm plot also gives us the end-to-end distance of the polymer chain.

Note that the information about size and that about mass obtained from light scattering are different and completely independent. The angular dependence of scattered intensity gives the end-to-end distance regardless of the molecular weight of the sample, whereas the intensity of scattering, after extrapolation to $C = 0$ and $\theta = 0$, gives the true weight-average molecular weight regardless of the size of the molecules.

The major difficulty in the light-scattering experiment lies in the need for removing all dirt, dust, and other unwanted material from the polymer solutions prior to their measurement. Dirt and dust scatter light too, and since their particles are usually much larger and heavier than polymer molecules, a little dirt can scatter a lot of light, completely interfering with the molecular-weight measurement. Cleaning the polymer solutions is not easy, but it can usually be done by filtering them through very-fine-pore filters.

ANOTHER WAY OF MEASURING $\bar{M}_w$

Although I will not describe the measurement in detail, I want to mention one more way of measuring $\bar{M}_w$ that is available to polymer scientists. This is the use of an instrument called the analytical ultracentrifuge. In this instrument, a polymer solution is placed in a cell that is held near the outer edge of a strong aluminum rotor. This device is spun on its axis at very high speeds, up to one thousand revolutions per second. The solution is thus subjected to forces many thousand times that of gravity—thousands of times more than the highest "G" forces an astronaut experiences during rocket takeoff. If the polymer molecules are more dense than the solvent (the usual case), they move toward the outer edge, the "bottom" of the cell. Their position and motion are followed by optical means. From these data can be calculated $\bar{M}_w$ and A_2.

The ultracentrifuge experiments are time-consuming and complicated, and the instrument is expensive. They work best for compact molecules like proteins and other biological materials, and are less easy to perform with random-coil polymers. For this reason, the technique is more often used by the biologist than by the synthetic polymer scientist.

SOME INFORMATION ABOUT
MOLECULAR-WEIGHT DISTRIBUTIONS

Now that we have learned how to measure both $\bar{M}_w$ and $\bar{M}_n$, we can get their ratio, $\bar{M}_w/\bar{M}_n$, described in

Chapter 3 as a measure of the breadth of the molecular-weight distribution curve of a polymer. I am sure you will agree, however, that there is a lot of work involved in getting this rather small amount of information. In addition, the combined errors of the two methods make the determination of $\bar{M}_w/\bar{M}_n$ imprecise just at the point where one wants to know it most closely, that is, for relatively narrow distributions.

For many years, however, this was the best information we could get, short of very tedious and even less precise experiments. More recently, the new methods described in Chapter 8 have changed this picture for the better. As a result the light-scattering technique has taken on new importance as the primary means of calibrating these new experiments.

Chapter 7

THE VISCOUS DRAG OF
DISSOLVED POLYMERS

To set the stage for our next topic of consideration, let's think again about the bead model of a polymer molecule we have used several times so far. In Chapter 4, we considered the size of the model, noting that if it were thrown into a swimming pool, it would expand into a random-coil conformation, occupying many times more space than the volume of the beads alone.

Now this was not a good analogy in one respect: We forgot to magnify the molecules of water in the swimming pool by the same factor of 100,000,000 by which the bead model is magnified over the actual molecule. Here, as in the opening paragraphs of Chapter 1, we must resort to fantasy in order to guess what we might see if we could observe a polymer molecule dissolved in a suitable solvent. But I hope you will agree with me on the following feature of this unusual sight: If we tried to stir, or pour, or otherwise disturb the polymer solution, we would find that the presence of the giant chain molecule interfered with the free movement of the small solvent molecules. Some of the small molecules would get held back by, or perhaps dragged along with, the big one.

This viscous drag of dissolved polymer molecules is what we see in real life. As we dissolve a polymer, in ever-increasing amounts, in a solvent, we see that the viscosity, or resistance to flow, of the solution becomes continuously greater. The solvent alone may have been free-flowing, like water. As polymer is added, and after the slow process of dissolving it is complete, the solution may behave like cooking oil; with more polymer, like honey; and with still more, it may appear over a short time not to flow at all.

Since similar amounts of low-molecular-weight materials do not cause this increase in viscosity, it must be associated with the long-chain nature of polymers. Consequently, the magnitude of the viscosity change must tell us something about the size, or perhaps the mass, of the polymer molecule. Which is it? And why? These are the questions we must now attempt to answer.

The viscous drag of polymer molecules is important in the design of an automobile lacquer, too. For spraying, the viscosity of the lacquer solution must fall within certain limits. To save money, formulators of lacquers like to use as much polymer as possible and as little solvent, which is ultimately evaporated and wasted. To avoid too high viscosity while keeping as much polymer as possible in the solution, the polymer scientist wishes to use as short chains as possible, minimizing their effect in increasing viscosity. This is consistent with the need we saw in Chapter 6 to keep the chains short to avoid cobwebbing, but remember too that reducing their length too far could lead to poor properties, as discussed in Chapter 5.

THE VISCOSITY OF POLYMER SOLUTIONS

We should first inquire how we can describe the viscosity of a polymer solution quantitatively—how we can put numbers on it. As you might expect, there are many ways of doing this, some useful for very viscous solutions, of the consistency of honey or lacquers, and others better suited for more freely-flowing liquids. I shall describe only one technique, the best for dealing with very dilute polymer solutions, whose viscosity is only a little greater than that of the solvent alone. Perhaps this choice will appeal to you, as it does to me, in view of the need to extrapolate results to zero concentration of polymer we have met in every method discussed so far.

The instruments used for measuring the dilute-solution

viscosity of polymers are simpler than any of the others we have described, and correspondingly less expensive. They are merely short lengths of glass capillary tubing, in which the capillary is one- to two-tenths millimeter in diameter and a few centimeters long, equipped with one or more bulbs on each end to hold the polymer solution conveniently. In operation, the polymer solution is forced up through the capillary by gentle air pressure to fill a bulb immediately above the capillary. Then it is allowed to flow back down by gravity. As the liquid level passes an upper marker line, a stopwatch is started; as it passes a lower line, the watch is stopped. The elapsed time, called the *efflux time* for that solution, the time necessary for a fixed volume of solution to flow through the capillary, is directly proportional to the viscosity of the solution. Efflux times of about a hundred seconds are usual. The efflux-time measurements for a series of polymer solutions and their solvent are all that are needed to evaluate the viscous drag of those polymer molecules.

It is customary to use the Greek lower-case letter eta, η, to designate viscosity. From what we have just said, the viscosity η of a solution is proportional to its efflux time t. For the solvent, let us use a subscript zero: then η_0 is proportional to t_0. We are interested in the increase of the solution's viscosity over that of the solvent, for this is the effect caused by the polymer. The ratio is called the *relative viscosity, η_r,* and is easily calculated:

$$\eta_r = \eta / \eta_0 = t / t_0$$

It is, of course, always greater than one.

We have yet to account for the concentration of the polymer. To do this, it is customary to calculate two more quantities. First we shall look at the increase in the relative viscosity over one; this is called the *specific viscosity, η_{sp}:*

$$\eta_{sp} = \eta_r - 1 = \frac{\eta}{\eta_0} - 1 = \frac{t}{t_0} - 1 = \frac{t - t_0}{t_0}$$

Then we find out how big this quantity is per unit of polymer concentration, C, by dividing η_{sp} by C. The result is called the *reduced viscosity*, but is usually written η_{sp}/C:

$$\frac{\eta_{sp}}{C} = \frac{t - t_0}{t_0 C}$$

Among polymer scientists, there has been some objection to the names given to these quantities. They point out, quite correctly, that the "relative viscosity" isn't a viscosity at all, but just a ratio of two numbers, and so on. But the names are well established, and as convenient as any for our use.

Measurements of the dilute-solution viscosity of polymers became important very early in the history of polymer science, as a result of the work of Hermann Staudinger, who won the Nobel prize for his understanding of the long-chain nature of polymers. As early as 1909 Staudinger used viscosity measurements to substantiate his ideas. He used the reduced viscosity, η_{sp}/C, for this purpose, thinking that it was independent of concentration. Today, however, we know that η_{sp}/C still changes with concentration, particularly for higher-molecular-weight samples. Thus, again, we must carry out experiments at several different concentrations and extrapolate to $C = 0$ in order to get a quantity that we will be satisfied to relate to the molecular structure of polymers. We call this quantity (the last of the viscosity functions we will consider) the *intrinsic viscosity,* and use the viscosity symbol enclosed in square brackets, $[\eta]$, to designate it.

When we come to examine the concentration dependence of η_{sp}/C, we must depart, almost for the first time, from results that can be described in terms of a theory. For obvious reasons, I have not always presented all the theory to you, but here for the first time I must say we have no theory; we simply must look at the experiments and see how η_{sp}/C changes with C for samples of different molecular weight. What we see is shown in Figure 38. This is the experimental result. Unlike the concentration dependence of the osmotic pressure, or light-scattering data, or all the others we have talked about, the slopes of these lines are not all the same, but increase

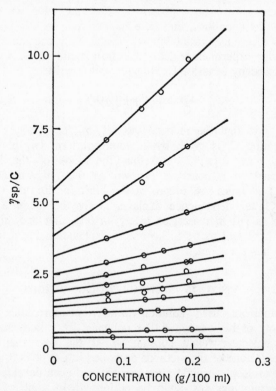

Fig. 38. This graph shows the way the reduced viscosity, η_{sp}/C, varies with the concentration C for a series of polymers of the same type but different molecular weights, all measurements being made with the same solvent and at the same temperature. (Adapted from my *Textbook of Polymer Chemistry,* Interscience, 1957.)

markedly for samples of higher viscosity. Working only with samples of low viscosity, Staudinger did not see this concentration dependence.

Even though we can't explain this result with a theory, it would be nice to have an equation that describes this family of curves, as an aid in making the extrapolation to $C = 0$ to get the intrinsic viscosity $[\eta]$. Several such equations have been proposed. They are what we call *empirical* equations, that is, equations that are not based on a theoretical result but have value only because they describe experimental data. The most useful of these was proposed by Maurice L. Huggins and is written

$$\frac{\eta_{sp}}{C} = [\eta] + k'[\eta]^2 C$$

This says that the reduced viscosity η_{sp}/C, at any concentration C, is given by an intercept term $[\eta]$ plus a slope term $k'[\eta]^2 C$, and that the slope of the line is equal to a constant (known as the Huggins constant) k' times the square of the intrinsic viscosity $[\eta]$. This latter dependence explains nicely the increase in slope as $[\eta]$ increases; so nicely, in fact, that one might feel there *had* to be a theoretical explanation for it, but none has appeared.

SOLUTION VISCOSITY AND MOLECULAR WEIGHT

Staudinger used solution-viscosity measurements in support of his postulate that polymers were long-chain, high-molecular-weight substances. At the time that he worked, none of the methods described in Chapters 5 and 6 for molecular-weight measurement had been developed. End-group analyses could be performed, in some cases, with low sensitivity; but for polymers of higher molecular weight, Staudinger could not find any end groups. His publications show how this puzzled him. Van't Hoff had also made osmotic-pressure measurements, but they gave such high molecular weights that they were disbelieved, and they were not exact because their concentration-dependence was not recognized.

Staudinger stated that the reduced viscosity of a polymer solution was directly proportional to the molecular weight of the polymer:

$$\eta_{sp}/C = KM$$

where K is simply a proportionality constant. For samples of very low molecular weight, he could support this statement with end-group analyses. At higher molecular weights, the reduced viscosity continued to increase even where the molecular-weight data were no longer available. This was powerful evidence that polymers were indeed high-molecular-weight substances.

Again, later work has substantiated Staudinger's postulate with only minor changes. As we have seen, it is necessary to replace η_{sp}/C with $[\eta]$ in Staudinger's equation to take account of the remaining concentration dependence of the reduced viscosity. And, as better molecular-weight data have become available, it has been found that Staudinger's equation has to be modified by raising the molecular weight to a power, denoted by the exponent a, somewhat less than one. The result,

$$[\eta] = KM^a$$

(where K will have a different numerical value than before), is an equation with which the names of several polymer scientists are associated, the most well known being the Austrian physicist Herman Mark, who has done most of his work in the United States.

Professor Mark's equation is also empirical, that is, it fits the experimental data although it is not derived from theoretical considerations. (However, it can be justified by newer theories, as we shall see in the next section.) If we rewrite the equation by taking the logarithm of each side, we get

$$\log [\eta] = \log K + a \log M$$

This is again the equation of a straight line, with intercept $\log K$ and slope a. Some typical experimental data, plotted in this way, are shown in Figure 39. Note that, for a sample of given molecular weight, $[\eta]$ depends on the nature of the solvent and the temperature. The location of the line, and thus the values of K and a, also depend on the type of polymer being studied.

The value of Mark's equation is that K and a have been measured for many polymer-solvent combinations. It

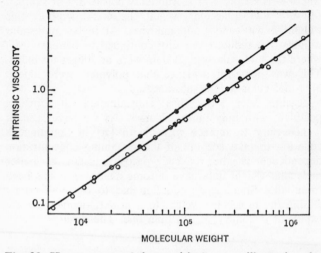

Fig. 39. Here are two of the empirical curves illustrating the use of the Mark equation for calculating molecular weights from viscosity data. Each point on the lines represents the measured molecular weight and intrinsic viscosity of one polymer sample. The two curves show the data for the same type of polymer with different solvents and temperatures. (Adapted from my *Textbook of Polymer Science,* second edition, Wiley-Interscience, 1971.)

is possible, then, for many kinds of polymers, to measure the intrinsic viscosity and calculate molecular weight from the known values of K and a. The experiments are simple, but we shall see shortly that there are some pitfalls to be avoided.

One final question: What kind of molecular weight does this method give? This can be calculated, as we did for the light-scattering experiment in Chapter 6, without much difficulty. The result shows that the viscosity-average molecular weight is lower than, but not far different from, the weight-average. But it depends on the value of a, and therefore (for a given type of polymer) on the solvent and temperature, not a very satisfying state of affairs. For most purposes, however, it is accurate enough to determine K and a from the known weight-average molecular weights and intrinsic viscosities of some samples that have been studied by light scattering, and then to use these values to calculate weight-average molecular weights from intrinsic viscosities for other polymers of the same type.

SOLUTION VISCOSITY AND MOLECULAR SIZE

Despite its empirical correlation with molecular weight, the intrinsic viscosity is a puzzling quantity in several respects. Chief among these is its strong dependence on the type of solvent used in the measurement. Why should this be?

The answer lies in a study made by Albert Einstein many years ago. In 1906, he developed a theory for the viscosity of suspensions of hard spherical particles, into which the solvent cannot penetrate. He showed that the specific viscosity of such a suspension is proportional to the fraction of its volume occupied by the spheres, independent of how heavy they are.

Now the behavior of solid spheres is in many respects quite different from that of random-coil polymers, but the key point in Einstein's theory has been duplicated in several theories of the viscosity of polymer solutions, among them those of Peter J. W. Debye and Paul J. Flory. This important point is that the size, not the mass, of the molecule is important. Einstein's theory states this as follows:

$$\eta_{sp} = \text{constant} \times \frac{v}{V}$$

where v is the volume occupied by the spherical particles in a total volume V of solution; v/V is the fraction of the total volume occupied by the spheres.

But in our consideration of polymers, we have not expressed the amount of material present in terms of the volume fraction, rather in terms of the concentration C, which is the mass of material in the volume V. If we express this mass in molecular-weight units, using the scale defined in Chapter 1, we see that $C = M/V$ or $V = M/C$. If we put this into Einstein's formula we get

$$\eta_{sp} = \text{const} \times \frac{vC}{M}$$

or

$$\frac{\eta_{sp}}{C} = \text{const} \times \frac{v}{M}$$

Paul J. Flory's theory for the viscosity of polymer solutions has exactly this form. The most important equation in his theory is

$$[\eta] = \Phi \frac{(\sqrt{\overline{r^2}})^3}{M}$$

It differs from our modification of Einstein's equation only in that the extrapolation to $C = 0$ has been added, converting η_{sp}/C into $[\eta]$, and v has been written as the cube of a linear dimension of the polymer chain, here the root-mean-square end-to-end distance described in Chapter 4.

The quantity Φ (the Greek capital letter phi) is shown in Flory's theory to be a universal constant—that is, it has the same value for all types of polymer and solvent and at all temperatures. This is very satisfying, since any good theory should apply to a wide variety of cases without changing the values of the constants in an arbitrary way.

Thus measurement of the dilute-solution viscosity of polymers gives directly their size, and not their molecular weight. In fact, you have probably noticed that, as a result of our converting from volume fraction to concentration, the molecular weight appears in the denominator of Flory's equation, whereas it was in the numerator of Staudinger's and Mark's empirical viscosity-molecular weight relationships. In the following sections we shall explain this puzzling discrepancy and explore some uses of the viscosity measurement based on its giving the molecular size.

RECONCILING SIZE AND MASS OF LINEAR POLYMERS

We must now show how the measurement of molecular size by solution viscosity can be extended to measure the molecular weight of the polymer, and see how this result compares with the empirical equation of Staudinger as modified by Mark and others. The key to doing this lies in the exploration of the size of polymer molecules we made in Chapter 4. There we saw that the size of a polymer chain depends on the nature of the polymer, including such factors as hindrance to rotation about the bonds in the chain; the nature of the solvent, through the magnitude of the polymer-solvent interactions; the temperature, since this also influences the polymer-solvent interaction forces; the way the chain is put together—linear, branched, or as a network; and of course the chain length and thus the molecular weight of the polymer.

In this section we shall restrict our attention to linear polymers, and introduce the other factors into Flory's equation to see how the intrinsic viscosity really depends on the molecular weight.

We saw in Chapter 4 that the effect of polymer-solvent interactions can be accounted for in terms of the unperturbed dimension of the chain, $\sqrt{r_o^2}$, and the expansion coefficient, α. The product of these two is the real end-to-end distance: $\sqrt{r^2} = \alpha \sqrt{r_o^2}$. Putting this into the Flory equation gives

$$[\eta] = \Phi \frac{(\sqrt{r_o^2})^3}{M} \alpha^3$$

Now recall that in Chapter 4 we showed that the end-to-end distance of the polymer calculated from the random-flight theory was proportional to the square root of the chain length, and therefore to the square root of molecular weight. Adding the restrictions to bond rotation and so on to get to the unperturbed dimensions of the chain does not change this proportionality. We can therefore substitute $\sqrt{M}$ for $\sqrt{r_0{}^2}$ in the Flory equation. This changes the value of the constant from Φ to something else we can call K:

$$[\eta] = K \frac{(\sqrt{M})^3}{M} \alpha^3$$

or

$$[\eta] = K\sqrt{M}\, \alpha^3$$

or, using the exponent 0.5 instead of the square-root sign,

$$[\eta] = KM^{0.5}\alpha^3$$

This begins to look like Professor Mark's equation. In fact, if we carry out the experiments at the special Flory temperature Θ (theta), where $\alpha = 1$, we have the Mark equation with the special value 0.5 for the exponent a. Now, the special nature of the theta temperature, the unperturbed dimensions of the polymer chain, and the exponent $a = 0.5$ were not appreciated until Flory's theories were announced, so that the statement that the viscosity-molecular weight exponent ought to be one-half in a theta solvent was a prediction. It was soon verified, in not one but many cases, and has proven to be one of the strongest pieces of evidence for the correctness of Flory's theories.

But what about other solvents, in which polymer-solvent interaction forces are significant, the polymer chain expands, and α is greater than unity? The intrinsic viscosity goes up correspondingly, and in fact a common way to measure α is to look at the change in viscosity on going from a Θ-solvent to the one in question: since $\alpha = 1$ at the theta temperature, the viscosity measured at that point is

$$[\eta]_\Theta = KM^{0.5}$$

Combining this with the previous equation we see that

$$[\eta] / [\eta]_\Theta = \alpha^3$$

We also know experimentally that, as we go to solvents exhibiting higher values of α, the viscosity-molecular weight exponent *a* goes from 0.5 to higher values, reaching about 0.8 in many cases. The Flory theory also explains this, for it shows that α depends on about the one-tenth power of M. Thus α^3 varies as $M^{0.3}$, so the product of $M^{0.5}\alpha^3$ depends on $M^{0.8}$, nicely predicting the higher exponent in the Mark equation for solvents interacting strongly with the polymer.

Thus, we see that, although the intrinsic viscosity basically measures the size of the randomly-coiling polymer chain, its empirical dependence on molecular weight is predicted from the known relations between mass and size, and their dependence on solvent type and temperature, for *linear* polymers. The emphasis on the word linear is, however, essential, as we shall see in the next section.

VISCOSITY, SIZE, AND CHAIN BRANCHING

If we recall again the discussion of Chapter 4, we saw that a given number of polymer chain segments forms a large random coil if the chain is linear; any other arrangement, in which a branched chain is formed, takes up less space. Therefore, for the same number of chain segments —that is, at the same molecular weight—the viscosity of a branched polymer is less than that of a linear polymer of the same type (in the same solvent and at the same temperature, of course). This difference in viscosity can be quite significant; in some of the branched polyethylenes studied by myself and my co-workers, the intrinsic viscosities were as low as one-quarter to one-fifth of those of the corresponding linear polymers.

This reduction in viscosity is, at present, the best way we have of detecting chain branching. One must determine the molecular weight of the sample, usually by light scattering. It is then possible, using the constants K and a for the Mark equation established in studies on linear polymers, to calculate the intrinsic viscosity that a linear polymer of this molecular weight would have. This is then compared with the actual intrinsic viscosity of the branched sample.

We would like to go farther than this and relate the ratio of the two viscosities to the degree of branching of the polymer. At the moment, we have not been able to do this with as great success as we would like, but the latest work in this field is encouraging.

THE VISCOSITY OF POLYMER MELTS

Although our discussion has been limited to the viscosity of dilute solutions of polymers, I must point out that the vastly greater viscosities of molten polymers are highly important quantities also. On the one hand, the melt viscosity can be related—again empirically—to molecular weight, and on the other it gives information on how the polymer can be fabricated into a useful article. In later chapters we will consider these processes in more detail.

Chapter 8

EXPLORING MOLECULAR-WEIGHT DISTRIBUTIONS

For as long as I have been associated with the field, polymer scientists have wished they knew more about the distribution of molecular weights in the samples they had to deal with. For, as we saw in Chapter 3, all the synthetic polymers we know how to make—and, excepting some biological materials, all naturally occurring polymers as well—always consist of a broad distribution of molecular weights. Yet, among all the methods for the molecular characterization of polymers we have described, none gives any direct information on the nature of this distribution. Only average molecular weights can be measured, and even the information obtained by comparing two different average molecular weights, as described in Chapter 6, simply isn't enough.

I can well remember situations in which some process went wrong, or some product failed to show the desired properties, for no apparent reason. The molecular weights would check out as expected. What else could be wrong? All we could say was "it must be the molecular-weight distribution." And no one could say we were wrong, because the experiments to prove or disprove our guess were too lengthy, costly, and inaccurate.

Measurement and control of the molecular-weight distribution turned out to be the key to success in making an acrylic automobile lacquer, too. Recall our discussions, in the previous three chapters, of tailoring the properties of these polymer solutions to spray without cobwebbing, using economical amounts of solvents, and to give lacquer films with good physical properties. These studies dictated that the number-average molecular weight of the polymer be as high as possible to obtain strong, tough, durable films, and that its weight-average molecular weight be as low as possible to get good, economical sprayability.

Thus, the molecular weight could not be allowed to go too low, or too high. In the early days of the development of these lacquers it appeared that there was no happy medium, either. Adjust polymerization conditions to raise the molecular weight, insuring good film properties, and the product couldn't be sprayed; lower it enough for spraying, and the properties deteriorated.

The solution to the problem lay in making a polymer with a narrower molecular-weight distribution, thereby increasing $\bar{M}_n$ and decreasing $\bar{M}_w$ just enough to allow a workable compromise between film properties and sprayability to be achieved. Fortunately, we knew how to do this, by further adjustment of polymerization techniques that we need not describe. The important point is that we had to know what was needed, and we had to be able to follow every step of the process through measurement of the molecular-weight distribution. As I have said, this was far from easy to do.

Fortunately, we are past this point today. Now we can, with the aid of new and powerful techniques, get a "picture" of the molecular-weight distribution in a polymer sample within a few hours. We can see any monomer that failed to polymerize, a missing component, an unexpected species that could be causing the trouble. Molecular-weight distribution is no longer the enigma, the scapegoat that it was for so many years.

My statements pose many questions. Why was it so difficult to learn about molecular-weight distributions until recently? What are the new methods, and how do they differ from the old? What can we really find out about the various kinds of molecules in a polymer sample? Answering these and related queries takes us into the last chapter in the story of characterizing polymer molecules.

HOW TO SEPARATE POLYMER MOLECULES
ACCORDING TO THEIR MASS

In principle, it is easy to decide how to study the molecular-weight distribution in a polymer. It's just like sorting apples or potatoes by size. You put the biggest ones in one pile, the next-biggest in another, and so on down to the smallest. Then you look at the relative sizes of the piles. This tells you all you want to know. The trick is to do it with molecules.

There are four ways I know of to separate molecules (little ones as well as polymers) one from another on the basis of some property. I shall describe each of them briefly, pointing out which ones are useful for separating polymer molecules in the way we want.

The first, and probably most commonly practiced, separation method is based on differences in solubility of the molecules to be separated. This principle is called *partition,* and it can be applied in several ways, almost all of which are useful for separating, or *fractionating,* polymers. The guiding principle here is the fact that, as a polymer chain gets longer, it becomes less soluble in a given solvent at a specified temperature. By lowering the temperature, for example, one may be able to cause the solution to become cloudy and then separate into two liquid phases, looking much like a mixture of tiny droplets of oil suspended in water. The little drops aren't oil, of course, but are a more concentrated solution of polymer containing more of the less-soluble (that is, higher-molecular-weight) molecules, while more of the shorter chains remain in the original solution as a result of their greater solubility. We shall expand our discussion of the partition of polymer solutions in the next section.

Probably the next-most-common separation technique, considering all sorts of materials, is called *adsorption.* This separation method is based on the development of strong forces that hold molecules onto surfaces. The classical cases of separation by adsorption involve gases. For example, gas masks work by providing a large area of surface on which the molecules to be removed from the air are easily adsorbed, while the oxygen to be breathed passes on through. Adsorption techniques can be used with dissolved molecules, too, but they have not been highly useful for fractionating polymers by molecular weight, because the adsorption forces don't change very much as molecular weight changes. For this reason we won't consider them further.

A third separation method is that of *ion exchange*. Polymers are involved here in several ways, but the separation process depends on the number of electric charges on the molecule and related properties. Most of the polymers that we have been discussing don't have charges of this sort, and cannot be separated by the ion-exchange principle. So this is another method of no immediate interest to our story.

Finally, all sorts of things can be separated according to *size* by a variety of methods, ranging from such commonplace operations as sieving or straining for things much larger than molecules, down to the unwanted permeation of very small polymer molecules through an osmotic membrane mentioned in Chapter 5. The name *permeation* is given to these methods. Since we have seen (for example, in Chapter 7) a close relationship between the size of a dissolved polymer molecule and its molecular weight, we might expect that permeation methods would be useful for polymer fractionation if the right kind of "sieve" or "strainer" can be found, with "holes" about the size of polymer molecules. Quite recently this sort of material has been prepared, and new techniques have evolved that have made the study of molecular-weight distributions very much easier than ever before.

We must realize, of course, that it is not enough just to separate or fractionate polymers by molecular weight, if we want to know about their molecular-weight distribution. In addition, we must measure both the weight and the molecular weight of each fraction obtained. These are the data that can be combined to give molecular-weight distribution curves like those of Figures 9 to 12. This is also where a lot of the time and effort come in, and as we look more closely at fractionation by partition and by permeation in the next sections, we shall pay special attention to ways in which these steps of analysis can be shortened.

FRACTIONATING POLYMERS BY SOLUBILITY

Several of the different ways in which we can make use of the dependence of the solubility of a polymer on its molecular weight are: precipitating the higher-molecular-weight material out of solution, either by lowering the temperature or by changing the composition of the solvent in such a direction as to lower the solubility of the polymer; extracting the lower-molecular-weight material into a second solvent, which itself does not mix with the first; and extracting the lower-molecular-weight material from a thin film of the solid polymer. The second of these three methods, called *coacervation,* is not widely practiced and I will not describe it in detail.

The first method, precipitation from solution, has the longest history of use. When I first got into the polymer business, this was the only method we had for fractionation. Usually, we would set up a large glass vessel like that shown in Figure 40, fitted with a stirring device, a thermometer, a means for adding liquid, and a means for drawing off liquid from the bottom. Experience told us that we had to work with very dilute solutions, so that the fractionation of even a teaspoonful of polymer required several gallons of solvent. Moreover, the whole assembly had to be placed in a large water bath so that it could be maintained at constant temperature.

Our procedure would be the following: The polymer solution would be placed in the vessel, filling it only part way. A second liquid, which was not a solvent for the polymer but which mixed with the solvent from which the polymer solution was made, was added slowly to the vessel while the stirring motor was operating. As the solvent power of the mixture of liquids grew less through the addition of more of the nonsolvent, the solution would suddenly become cloudy as polymer began to precipitate out from the solution. At this point, the addition of nonsolvent was stopped, but the stirring was continued for a few minutes. The stirrer was then stopped.

Now the portion of the polymer that separated out

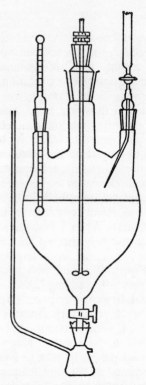

Fig. 40. This is a typical vessel for the fractionation of a polymer by precipitation from solution. The three "necks" at the top of the vessel accommodate a thermometer, the shaft of a stirring motor, and a device for introducing accurately known amounts of a nonsolvent into the vessel. At the bottom is a small flask into which the precipitated polymer phase can be drawn off, as described in the text. The vessel proper is immersed in a constant-temperature bath during operation. (Adapted from my *Textbook of Polymer Science*, second edition, Wiley-Interscience, 1971.)

from the remainder of the solution carried solvent along with it; that is, it was itself dissolved as a more concentrated (and therefore more viscous) polymer solution. This second phase slowly coalesced and fell to the bottom of the vessel. After some hours (usually the next day) we could remove it, thus completing the separation of the entire polymer sample into two fractions.

If we had guessed correctly, the fraction removed contained only 5 to 10 per cent of the total polymer. We then added more nonsolvent to the large vessel in order to precipitate another sample, repeating the procedure just described. Thus we could separate a polymer sample into ten to twenty fractions at the rate of about one per day. The individual fractions were isolated from the solvent by diluting their viscous solutions, then adding a large quantity of a very strong nonsolvent, which caused them to precipitate in a finely divided, almost solvent-free form, in which they could easily be dried.

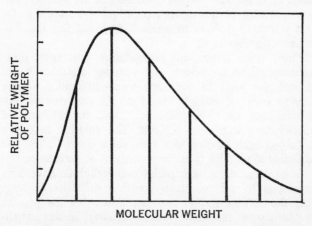

RELATIVE WEIGHT OF POLYMER

MOLECULAR WEIGHT

Fig. 41. Ideally, we would hope to be able, by fractionation, to divide a polymer sample up into sharply defined fractions like those indicated on this molecular-weight distribution curve. Each fraction contains all the molecules within a certain range of molecular weights and no others. But, as the text and Figure 42 show, we cannot achieve this kind of separation in real experiments.

What was the nature of these fractions? It would, of course, depend on the efficiency of the phase-separation step—that is, to what extent all the higher-molecular-weight molecules went into the precipitated phase and all the lower-molecular-weight ones stayed behind. Ideally, we would have liked to achieve the kind of separations sketched in Figure 41, where each fraction contains all of the molecules within a certain range of molecular weights, and no others of higher or lower molecular weight.

The theories of Paul J. Flory and Maurice L. Huggins for the thermodynamics of polymer solutions showed clearly, however, that this ideal condition was not even closely approached. One of the predictions of the theory was that, no matter what molecular weight—high or low —a given species had, some of it would be found in both the precipitated and dissolved phases. This meant that there would inevitably be considerable overlapping in the range of molecular weights contained in the various fractions. Instead of the clean separation of Figure 41, the best we could do was to produce fractions like those illustrated in Figure 42.

Thus, fractionation by precipitation was both time-consuming and inefficient, and polymer scientists began to look for ways to overcome these difficulties. It was easy to think of ways to speed up the experiments, but to overcome the theoretical limits on the efficiency of fractionation was more difficult. The solution here was to subject each fraction to several steps of separation and recombination, with some improvement at each step.

Several variations of experimental technique have been developed to achieve these goals; I will describe only one, the *column-elution* method. Elution is the process in which some material is dissolved away; in this experiment, the lowest-molecular-weight portions of the polymer are first dissolved away from the rest of the sample, followed by molecules of higher and higher molecular weight in successive fractions. To make this work, it is necessary to spread the polymer out in a very thin layer, so that a liquid that can dissolve only part of it can still

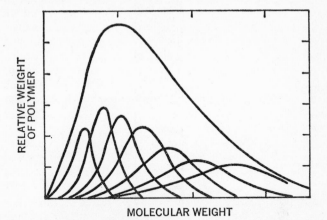

RELATIVE WEIGHT OF POLYMER

MOLECULAR WEIGHT

Fig. 42. In reality, as the theories of Flory and Huggins show, about the best we can do by single separation steps (such as precipitation from solution) is to produce overlapping fractions of polymer like these. Even these results are calculated assuming perfect experiments; in any real experiment, we probably do not even do this well. (This and Figures 43 and 44 are adapted from my *Textbook of Polymer Science,* second edition, Wiley-Interscience, 1971.)

penetrate into the film of polymer and reach all its molecules. This is accomplished by immersing tiny glass beads (or sometimes sand or other materials) in a polymer solution and, by lowering the temperature or adding a non-solvent, precipitating the polymer in a very thin layer onto the beads.

These polymer-coated beads are then placed inside a glass tube (as in Figure 43) called a column. Typically such a column may be half an inch to an inch in diameter and one to two feet long. With the column held at a constant temperature, it is filled with a nonsolvent for the polymer, taking care that all air bubbles are removed. Then, a mixture of solvent and nonsolvent, chosen so that it will dissolve only the lowest-molecular-weight part of the polymer, is poured slowly into the column. As it

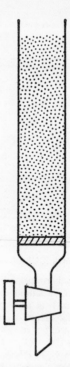

Fig. 43. The basic parts of an apparatus for polymer fractionation by column elution. The polymer sample is deposited in a very thin film on fine glass beads or other supports that are placed in the column. Solvent mixtures that will dissolve material of successively higher molecular weight are poured in through the top. A valve at the bottom controls the rate at which these liquids flow through the column.

Fig. 44. Common modifications to the column fractionation equipment shown in Figure 43 include a system for mixing "good" and "poor" solvent liquids in varying amounts to produce a continuous gradation or gradient of solvent power in the liquid flowing through the column. This sketch is based on the apparatus my colleagues and I used to study the molecular-weight distribution of polyethylene. It included means for dividing the liquid coming out of the column into constant-volume fractions and collecting them in test tubes, and for keeping the whole apparatus at constant temperature.

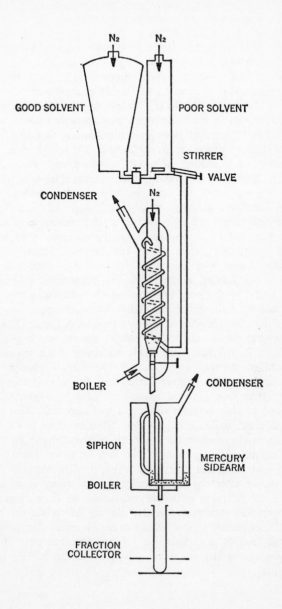

passes through the sample and out the bottom, the part of the polymer that can dissolve will do so and is removed as the first fraction. Next, a somewhat stronger solvent mixture is poured through to dissolve the molecules of somewhat higher molecular weight, and so on.

Since the column-elution method does not require waiting until a suspension of freshly precipitated polymer coagulates and settles to the bottom of a vessel, successive fractions can be removed much more rapidly than in fractionation by precipitation. Typically, twenty to thirty fractions are obtained in a day's time. Although a larger number of fractions helps to some extent in getting more efficient fractionation, the column-elution methods can be operated in such a way as to provide, for each fraction, a large number of steps of dissolving, reprecipitating, and redissolving as the solvent and polymer together move slowly down the column. Two ways of accomplishing this, which can be used separately or together, are: (1) providing for a continuous, smooth change in solvent composition, as illustrated in Figure 44; and (2) keeping one end of the column somewhat warmer than the other, as Figure 45 describes.

While the solubility of a given type of polymer changes somewhat as its molecular weight varies, much greater changes in solubility are likely to result if the chemical nature of the polymer changes. Sometimes changes of this sort are deliberately introduced by mixing together more than one kind of monomer before polymerization by one of the methods discussed in Chapter 2. This sort of polymer, called a *copolymer,* often contains molecules with a range of chemical compositions resulting from their having differing amounts of the two or more monomers.

If such chemical differences exist, it often happens that the major effect of fractionation by solubility is to separate the polymer molecules according to their chemical composition rather than molecular weight. While this can be disconcerting if one wants to study molecular weight, it can lead to very valuable information, otherwise hard to get, about the chemical nature of the molecules in a polymer.

FRACTIONATING POLYMERS BY SIZE

I suppose many polymer scientists have thought how nice it would be to have a microscopic fishnet or strainer that could be dipped into a polymer solution, and pulled out containing all the molecules too big to pass through its pores. Of course, we will agree that this would be a

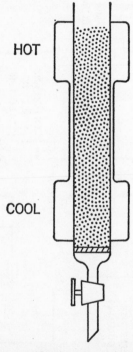

HOT

COOL

Fig. 45. A further modification to column-elution equipment consists of an arrangement to heat one end of the column slightly and cool the other. For a given solvent mixture, polymer dissolved near the top of the column will precipitate a little farther down in a cooler temperature zone. As more powerful solvent comes along, it will be redissolved only to reprecipitate still farther down. This succession of fractionation steps improves the efficiency of the separation process.

delicate experiment. Remember that the randomly-coiling polymer chain is a diffuse and easily deformed thing—as our bead model would be if thrown into a swimming pool. But it *would* be nice to do. With a graded series of such sieves, one could fractionate polymers according to size quite nicely. All we need is some molecular sieves.

Fanciful? Maybe. But it was not to the American chem-

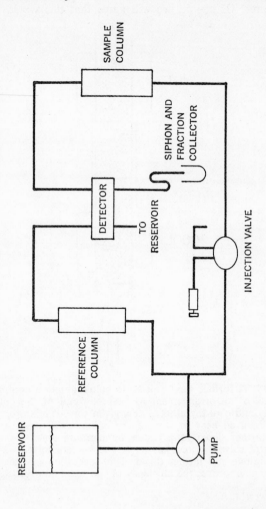

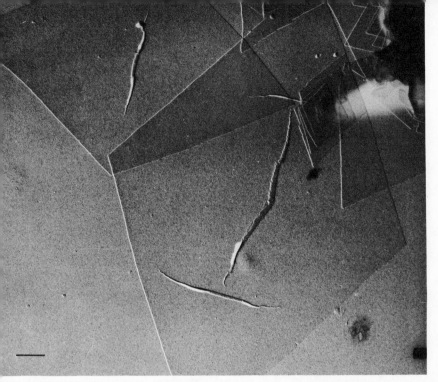

PLATE 12. This figure is an electron-microscope photograph of a single crystal of polyethylene, grown from dilute solution. The line indicating the scale of the photograph is 20,000 A long. The thickness of the sample is, however, only about 100 A. And the polymer chains, several thousands A long, run parallel to the thickness, not the width, of the crystal! (Courtesy of P. H. Geil.)

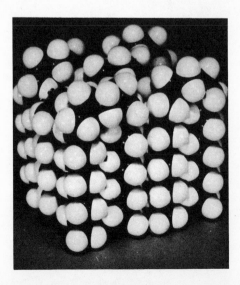

PLATE 13. The explanation for the puzzling facts presented in the caption to Plate 12 is that the polyethylene chains fold back and forth within the crystal, as explained in the text and illustrated in this picture of a model of the molecule. (Courtesy of P. H. Geil.)

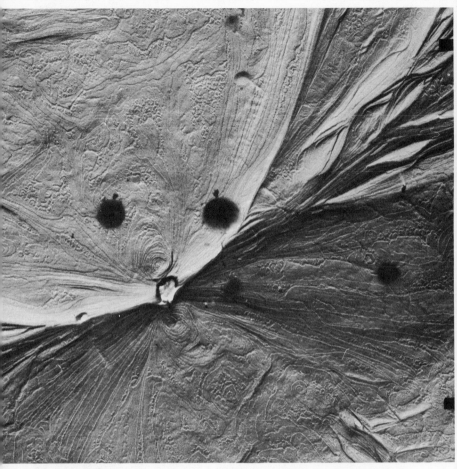

PLATE 14. This is an electron-microscope photograph showing the surface of a solid piece of polyethylene. Note that it appears to be made up entirely of lamellae, some seen almost on edge and others lying parallel to the plane of the paper. There do not seem to be any amorphous regions visible, and the picture we get is far different from that predicted by the fringed-micelle theory (Figure 58). (Courtesy of P. H. Geil.)

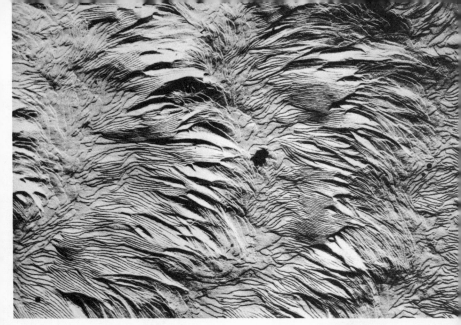

PLATE 15. This electron micrograph shows the arrangement of lamellae into a larger ordered structure called a spherulite. Again, we are looking at the surface of a solid sample. (Courtesy of E. W. Fischer.)

PLATE 16. This is a photograph of a spherulite taken with a light microscope using crossed polarizers. The light-and-dark pattern in the form of a cross is typical of spherulites. It results from rotation of the plane of polarized light by the polymer chains as they are oriented in different directions. (Courtesy of F. P. Price.)

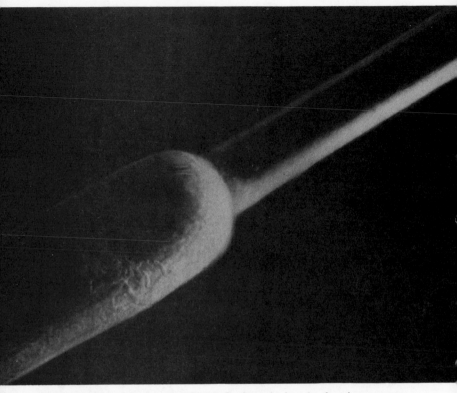

PLATE 17. The change in the shape of a fiber during the drawing process. (Courtesy of C. W. Bunn and the Elsevier Publishing Co.)

ical engineer John C. Moore. Following up some puzzling observations by workers in other separation fields,
particularly ion exchange, he thought he saw how to
make "molecular sieves"—porous particles with holes and
internal cavities about the size of random-coil polymer
molecules. Moreover, he visualized how to use these materials to fractionate polymers in a practical way. His
techniques worked, and have come close to revolutioniz-
ing the field of polymer characterization in the last few
years.

John Moore's concept started with a new kind of polymer material that he called a gel—not a new term, of
course—and that he made by polymerizing the monomer
styrene into a highly crosslinked (Chapter 2) form, in
the presence of large amounts of a rather poor solvent.
This unusual treatment produces highly porous, sponge-
like but hard and rigid polymer spheres, about a hun-
dredth of an inch in diameter (Plates 9 and 10). The
sizes of the pores in these particles (Plate 11) can be
varied, by changing the polymerization conditions, between the sizes of small molecules and the diameters of
the largest dissolved polymer coils. Here, then, are our
"fishnets"—molecular "sieves" in the true sense of the
word.

Moore used these gels in a system of polymer fractionation not unlike the column-elution method, except
of course that it does not separate by differences in solu-

Fig. 46. This sketch shows the essentials of an apparatus for
gel permeation chromatography. A pump moves solvent from
a reservoir through the apparatus. The solvent stream is split
into two. One of these is a reference stream that contains no
sample but goes through a separation column and the detector. It is used to provide a pure solvent stream in the detector,
against which the sample stream can be compared. The
sample is introduced into the other stream, using the device
described in Figure 47. Fractionation of the sample takes
place in the sample separation column, and the amount of
polymer in the sample stream is measured in the detector,
whose signal is displayed on a recorder. The sample stream
then passes through a volume-counting device; the information obtained here is also displayed on the recorder.

bility. Such a system, in which a liquid phase (here the polymer solution) flows past a material that stays in one place (the gel) is called a *chromatographic* system, and a process using it is called *chromatography*. This chromatographic process operates by means of permeation—that is, the polymer molecules in solution can permeate or penetrate into the pores of the gel particles—so Moore gave it the name *gel permeation chromatography*.

Gel permeation chromatography works in the following way. The gel material is packed into a column, which can be glass but in a commercially available instrument is made of steel, $\frac{3}{16}$ inch in diameter and four feet long. The column is kept full of a solvent for the polymer to be studied. (The gel, although itself a polymer, is so fully crosslinked that it cannot dissolve or even swell when immersed in the solvent.) A pumping system is provided to pump more of the same solvent continuously through the column and through a detector that measures the concentration of polymer in the solvent coming out of the column. This is plotted on a recorder as a function of the amount of solvent that has gone through the column. Figure 46 shows the instrument.

When the system is operating smoothly, a sample of polymer solution is "injected" into the flowing solvent stream at the entrance to the column, by means of the injection valve described in Figure 47. We must now look carefully at what happens to this sample as it flows through the column.

As shown schematically in Figure 48, at the time the sample enters the column, there is no polymer dissolved in the solvent inside the gel particles, but there is now polymer outside. This difference in the concentration of polymer inside and outside the gel produces a tendency for the polymer molecules to move to make the concentrations equal. Thus, the polymer molecules tend to permeate into the interior of the gel particles.

If the pores of the gel particles are just the right variety of sizes, we will find that the biggest polymer molecules can just barely fit into the biggest openings in the gel. The next-biggest molecules will be able to fit into a few

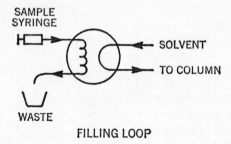

FILLING LOOP

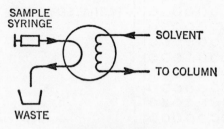

EMPTYING LOOP

Fig. 47. Samples are introduced into the gel permeation chromatograph by means of the injection loop and valve. When the valve is turned to the position shown at the top, the loop can be filled with polymer solution. Meanwhile, the sample stream from the pump to the sample separation column is passing through the other side of the valve. When the valve is turned to the position shown at the bottom, the loop becomes a part of the sample stream, and the polymer solution in it is pushed on into the column. (This and Figure 48 are reproduced courtesy of Jack Cazes and the *Journal of Chemical Education.*)

more of the inside pores of the gel, and so on down to the very smallest polymer molecules, to which almost all of the holes inside the gel are accessible. That is, the smaller the molecule is, the more of the internal volume of the gel particles it will fit into.

But the stream of solvent keeps moving past the gel particles as the pump pushes more solvent along. Now

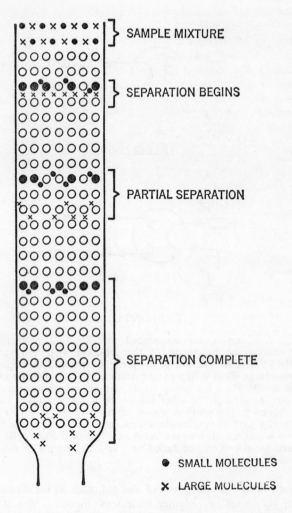

Fig. 48. This sketch illustrates the principle of separation by molecular size operating in gel permeation chromatography. It is explained more fully in the text.

the polymer molecules of the sample have gone into or past the gel, and there is no longer any polymer in the solvent outside the gel. The concentration difference is now reversed, and the polymer inside the gel tends to come back out. It's easy to see that the smaller polymer molecules, which can permeate into more of the gel, will stay inside the gel longer. And while inside, they are removed from the flowing solvent stream. When they come back out into the stream again, they have fallen behind their larger companions which could not penetrate as much of the pore volume, stayed inside a shorter time, and rejoined the moving stream sooner.

The picture repeats itself down the entire length of the column—in and out of the interior of the porous gels, driven by the differences in concentration, the smaller molecules falling farther and farther behind the big ones. At the end of the column, the molecules come out nicely separated according to size, the biggest ones first, the smallest ones last.

The detector and recorder furnish a record of how much polymer comes out at every instant. The experiments give the same result every time, in that a given size molecule always comes out at the same point—when the same volume of solvent has been pumped through—after the sample was injected. This result, by the way, is almost completely independent of the chemical nature of the polymer, depending only on its size. Since (for linear polymers) size and molecular weight are closely related, as we saw in Chapters 4 and 7, this means we have achieved the fractionation of our polymer by molecular weight that we desired.

What do we now have? A curve of amount of material plotted against retention volume, the volume of solvent passed through the column since the sample was injected. Figure 49 shows a typical curve of this sort. It is reminiscent of the molecular-weight distribution curves we saw in Chapter 3. But it is not quite the same. In the next section we will see how to transform gel permeation chromatography curves into molecular-weight distributions.

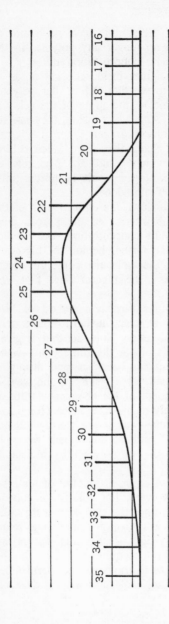

Fig. 49. Here is a typical recorder trace from a gel permeation chromatograph. The height of the trace, above a base line drawn between sections of the curve before (right) and after (left) the sample has come through, measures the concentration of polymer in the stream. The sharp marks on the recorder-pen trace at regular intervals count the volume of solvent that has passed through the column. The sample was injected into the system at count zero. Note the similarity between this curve and the molecular-weight distribution curves of Chapter 3. The sample measured here is a standard polystyrene distributed by the National Bureau of Standards. It has $\bar{M}_w/\bar{M}_n = 2.1$.

FROM FRACTIONS TO
MOLECULAR-WEIGHT DISTRIBUTIONS

Neither the fractions obtained from solubility-based separations nor the recorder traces from gel permeation chromatography are, directly, the molecular-weight distribution data polymer scientists wish to have. Something more must be added in each case.

The polymer fractions, no matter how obtained, must be characterized by one or another of the methods described in Chapters 5, 6, and 7. The data needed to provide a molecular-weight distribution curve are the weight and molecular weight of each fraction. Getting this information is another operation that makes the evaluation of molecular-weight distributions from fractionation data tedious and time-consuming.

With gel permeation chromatography, the necessary data are more easily obtained. The relative weights of each polymer species are equivalent to the concentrations measured directly on the recorder of the instrument. All that is needed is to provide a calibration of the retention-volume scale on the chart in terms of molecular weight. This is not difficult to do: One simply puts a series of samples of known molecular weight through the instrument—material of relatively narrow molecular-weight distribution works best—and measures the retention volume corresponding to each molecular weight. These calibration data can be used to convert retention volumes to molecular weights for the polymer samples being studied.

With these data in hand, molecular-weight distribution curves of the type we have discussed in Chapter 3 are easily constructed, and I think we need not go through the arithmetic of doing this. One can also calculate the number-average and weight-average molecular weights of the sample, using the equations we developed earlier.

Thus we have come to the end of our story. We see now how to obtain information on molecular-weight distributions, the last step needed to complete our study of the molecular characterization of polymers. Now it is time to explore the practical consequences of the knowledge we have obtained, to relate the structures of synthetic high polymers to their useful physical properties.

PART III

Polymer Properties
and Molecular Structure

Chapter 9

THE PROPERTIES OF
AMORPHOUS POLYMERS

Our journey through the wonderland of giant molecules has, so far, been one of discovery and understanding of the structure of synthetic polymers. We have seen—and made models of—their long-chain nature, explored the reasons for their distributions of size and of molecular weight, and finally learned how to measure these quantities.

But in order to do so, we have been forced to consider the behavior of polymer chains when they are widely separated from their neighbors, surrounded by the small molecules of a solvent. Only in this way could we study the properties of molecular weight and molecular size. Now the behavior of polymers in solution is, after all, far different from their properties in the solid state, free from the diluting effects of large amounts of solvent. And it is in the solid state, almost exclusively, that we make use of polymers as fibers, rubbers, and plastics.

Consequently, if we are to put a purpose to our studies, to use them to understand the way these important materials contribute to today's world, we must consider how the solid-state properties of synthetic polymers depend on and are derived from their molecular structure.

One of the first things we discover when we deal with the properties of polymers free from solvent—let's call them bulk polymers—is that they can exist in two quite different sorts of structures depending on the presence or absence of regularity or order in the arrangement of their molecular chains. We can demonstrate this easily with our bead model of a polymer molecule. Throw it on the table, stir it around, wad it up, crumple it, taking full advantage of the randomness of its structure, and you have a tangled mass of chains reminiscent of a well-stirred bowl of spaghetti. Except as the result of accident, the position of one part of the chain bears no relation to the location or arrangement of its neighbors. There is no order in the structure, and we give it a name appropriate to this: *amorphous,* derived from the Greek words meaning without order.

On the other hand, with a little work you can straighten out the bead model and lay it down on the table again in a highly ordered structure. Perhaps you will decide to loop the chain back and forth so that sections of it lie alongside and even on top of one another in a regular array. This structure is quite different in its regularity from the amorphous arrangement we had a few moments ago. Now, the position of every bead and every chain bears a definite, fixed, and repeating relationship to the locations of all its neighbors. We have a name for this type of structure too: crystalline.

Remembering the limitations of dealing with a model rather than looking at the properties of real polymers, we have at least discovered a basis for dividing bulk polymers into two classes: amorphous and (at least partially) crystalline. These two classes do exist, and have sufficiently different properties to warrant our considering them in separate chapters. Amorphous polymers (considered here) are either rubbery or glassy, or else they flow like tar or pitch. Crystalline polymers (Chapter 10), on the other hand, can be tough, strong materials like plastics and fibers.

POLYMER MELTS AND FABRICATION

We have used the word *plastic* a good many times in this book without ever saying exactly what it means. I expect you all know that it refers to the ability of a material to move or flow when pressure is put on it. Today we use many plastic materials around the house—putty, sealers of various sorts, chewing gum, and so on. One common property of all these things is that they do not flow too rapidly when pushed—that is, their viscosity is very high. They are not watery fluids that can be poured; they do flow in the same way as water but very, very much more slowly.

From what we have learned so far, it should not be surprising to find that this ability to flow but with a very high viscosity is characteristic of long-chain polymers. And, the higher the molecular weight of the polymer, the higher its viscosity, not only in dilute solution as we saw in Chapter 7, but—at much higher levels of viscosity— in the bulk as well, with no solvent present.

There is one additional requirement that we have not yet mentioned. The viscosities of all substances depend very strongly on the temperature. As temperature goes up, viscosity always goes down. Why? To answer this, we had better look at what temperature really means. We find, as you have probably already learned from your study of physics, that the amount of movement that the atoms of all substances are continuously undergoing is closely related to temperature. Except at the absolute zero of temperature, atoms never stand perfectly still; they are always moving minutely, vibrating randomly around their average positions. And, as the temperature increases, so does the amount of energy they use in these vibrations.

What has this to do with the plastic nature of giant molecules, with their ability to flow? Now we must look again at our bead molecule, in its tangled, amorphous arrangement, and consider what would happen if we pushed on one side of it hard enough to make it move— that is, flow. We would see that the beads on different parts of the chain have to move past one another, and they do this a few at a time, a short segment of the chain taking up a new position in a space created when its neighbors slipped away, and leaving some room for still other beads to slide into.

All these molecular motions, which add up to what we call flow, cannot take place unless the atoms themselves are moving enough to "give" a bit when their neighbors come near. Thus, we must put enough energy of motion into the atoms of the chain to allow them to move before flow can take place. In the materials I mentioned before, like chewing gum, there is enough molecular motion available at room temperature for flow to take place, but for most plastics there is no flow until the temperature is raised considerably above room temperature, usually even well above the temperature of boiling water. Since these substances don't flow at room temperature, but do soften and undergo flow, if pushed hard enough, at high temperatures, we say they melt, and we describe them, at temperatures where they will flow, as molten polymers. It is clear that, for most of the polymers we use in our daily lives, melting or softening points are well above room temperature.

Herman F. Mark recently pointed out that if polymers are to continue to gain in usefulness to man, and to take their place alongside metals and ceramics as the materials we use to build structures and machines, we must look for ways to raise the softening points of polymers still further, so that they retain their good mechanical properties at temperatures well above room temperature. He mentioned three ways of doing this. The first is to crosslink the chains together into networks, which we saw in Chapter 2 leads first to the rubbers we will discuss in the next section, and then to thermosetting plastics. The second way to raise softening points is to make the polymer chains stiffer, so that more energy—and thus higher temperature—is needed to give their molecular segments the freedom of motion that is required in a polymer melt. Finally, Mark said, one can synthesize the polymers in such a structure that they can crystallize. As we shall see in Chapter 10, the crystalline regions of polymers are strong, tough, and stiff, and lock the structure of these materials together much like crosslink bonds.

Before considering the results of these changes on the properties of polymers, let us consider the value of having a polymer in the molten state, where it will respond to pressure with a slow but continuous change in shape.

This is the way that we control the final form of the plastic material, the way we convert polymers into the useful articles with which we are familiar. With very few exceptions, the flow of polymer melts is essential to their fabrication into their final useful forms.

These fabrication processes can be divided into two major classes. In one, called *molding,* the molten polymer is pushed with high pressure into a cavity called a mold. There it is allowed to cool and thus solidify, taking the shape of the mold. The mold itself is made of two or more pieces of heavy metal. After the polymer has cooled, the mold is opened and the finished piece is taken out. Various molding processes are used to produce all sorts of plastic articles, ranging from big pieces like the lining of a refrigerator, or a trash container, on down through such things as telephones or cases for clocks and radios, to very small pieces, perhaps no more than a six-teenth of an inch in size but perfectly formed for use as parts of some complex machine.

One of the exceptions to fabrication by the use of molten polymers is really a special type of molding. Here one starts with the low-molecular-weight materials—brittle, powdered solids—which on heating polymerize and crosslink at the same time to form thermosetting plastics. Under the pressure applied to the mold, the polymer flows just enough in this process to take the exact shape desired in the finished piece.

The second major melt fabrication process has many variations also, but the basic principle is that of using pressure to push the molten polymer out of an opening called a die. This method is called *extrusion* when the material comes out in the form of a sheet, film, or tube (a garden hose, for example) or any other long, continuous shape. If the material is very long and thin, it is called a fiber, and then the process of making it is usually called *spinning,* but really works on the same principle.

Perhaps this is enough to show you that the melt-flow properties of polymers are important. So is their relation to molecular structure. The molecular weights of polymers must be controlled quite closely so that their melts have the right viscosity for the fabrication process at an appropriate temperature for molding or extrusion. Although the weight-average molecular weight is perhaps the most important quantity determining the melt viscosity, both the details of the molecular-weight distribution and the amount and nature of chain branching, if it is present, must be considered.

THE RUBBERY STATE

What a wonderful and unusual thing a rubber band is! Do you know of anything else that has this amazing combination of properties?

· It can be stretched up to ten or more times its original length.
· When fully stretched, it becomes very stiff and resists further stretching.
· When released, it snaps back rapidly.
· And it completely recovers its original size and shape, ready to be stretched and released hundreds of times without change!

If you do think of another material, there is no doubt whatsoever that it is a polymer, for the first requirement for any material to be an elastomer—a rubber—is that it consist of long-chain molecules. Do you think you know of an exception? What about "elastic sulfur"? Not so common now, this was once a favorite demonstration experiment of the chemists, to melt ordinary sulfur and cool it quickly to a rubbery solid. And, anybody knows, sulfur isn't a polymer. But—it is, and it *has* to be, in its elastic form. It exists as long sulfur chains, in which the atoms are bonded together strongly enough to give this form of sulfur the properties of a polymer, even though the sulfur-sulfur bonds are so heat sensitive that they are quickly broken apart when the temperature is raised a few degrees.

In fact, we can write down several requirements that define the molecular structure of all elastomers:

• They must be high polymers.

• They must be amorphous when they are unstretched, since the presence of crystallinity would make them tough and strong but nonstretchable. But if they can crystallize when they are fully stretched, they develop more strength than if they cannot.

• They must be at such a temperature that their molecular chains can slip rapidly past one another, since this kind of molecular motion is necessary to give the great distortions of their shape that occur on stretching.

• They must be held together by a small number of crosslinks, widely spaced, that join all their molecules together in a loose, flexible network. Otherwise, the freedom of molecular motion necessary if elastomers are to stretch so easily would be accompanied by flow of the sort we discussed before, and the rubber would not recover its original shape when it was released.

Why do elastomers behave as they do? This is easy to understand if we recall the random-coil nature of high polymers discussed in Chapter 4. Remember that an amorphous polymer consists of many intertwining, interpenetrating random-coil chains—the well-mixed bowl of spaghetti type of structure. In an elastomer, each of these molecules is tied to its neighbors by a few crosslinks. The important thing to think about is that part of a molecule lying between two such crosslinks, as sketched in Figure 50. We shall ask what happens to such a segment of a polymer chain when the rubber is stretched. As Figure 51 suggests, the segment will be stretched too, perhaps not by the same amount or even in the same direction, but stretched nevertheless.

Now let's think about the number of ways in which the chain atoms of this segment can be arranged. We saw in Chapter 4 that the greater the distance between the ends of the chain (or, correspondingly, the ends of the segment), the smaller the number of arrangements or conformations it can take up. When we stretch the segment by stretching the rubber, we are forcing the molecule to

Fig. 50. This sketch shows how the segment of chain between two crosslinks in a rubber looks when the rubber is not stretched and the segment can take up many different conformations despite the fact that its ends are tied down, so to speak.

do something it doesn't want to do—we are restricting it to a smaller number of arrangements. The laws of probability and of thermodynamics combine to tell us that it takes energy to do this, which is the reason you have to pull hard on a rubber to stretch it. And the backward pull of the elastomer, tending to restore it to its unstretched state, arises from the thermodynamic drive forcing the chain segments back into the state where they can take up the largest number of molecular arrangements. That is

Fig. 51. When the rubber is stretched, the ends of the chain segment are pulled apart. Now the segment has to take up conformations in which the distance between its ends is much greater. There are far fewer of these, and the laws of statistics and thermodynamics tell us that the segment tries to pull its ends closer together so that it can have more ways to arrange itself. This is the origin of the restoring force that makes a stretched rubber band snap back when it is released.

just the unstretched state from which we started. So, you see, the rubberiness of a rubber requires that it be made out of a polymer, either natural or synthetic.

By far the largest fraction of all elastomers, again both natural and synthetic, is used to make automobile tires. And tires are a lot different from rubber bands, obviously. Part of this difference results from the structure of the tire itself, which combines layers of very strong synthetic-fiber, glass, or steel cords with the rubber, but the properties of the rubber itself are different in a rubber band and a tire. The rubber in a tire is stronger, stiffer, tougher, and more resistant to abrasion than in most other forms in which we use elastomers. These changes come about as the result of a process called *reinforcement,* which can be thought of as a special kind of crosslinking, carried out at the same time as the formation of chemical cross-links between chains takes place in the process known as vulcanization. In reinforcement, the rubber molecules are bonded to very small particles of carbon or soot called carbon black, particles some hundreds of Angstroms in diameter, large compared to polymer chains but of course small compared to the tire. These particles act much like the crystalline regions that give our tough, strong plastics and fibers their good strength properties. And, incidentally, they account for the fact that tires and other reinforced rubber articles are black in color.

VISCOELASTICITY

In my collection of polymeric materials, I have a strip of plastic film with unusual properties. When I pull on its ends to stretch it, the film gets longer as a sheet of rubber would, but with a big difference: it stretches slowly, taking ten or fifteen seconds to reach its fully stretched length. Then, when I stop pulling, the film returns equally slowly all the way to its original size. Here's a new behavior, a kind of a delayed or slow elastic response that only polymers exhibit, to which we give the name *viscoelasticity,* a combination of the words viscosity and elasticity.

This means that polymers can respond in three different ways to a pressure or a stretching (or twisting) pull. First, they can respond elastically, with a rapid distortion or stretch, as rubbers do. Then, they can undergo the slow changes of viscoelasticity that I have just described. Finally, they can flow.

Now these three things are not as different as they sound, and in fact many polymers show all three kinds of changes, which more or less blend into one another. If you were to look very closely at my viscoelastic material as I stretch it, you would see that the first part of its increase in length comes quite quickly, but then the rate of stretch slows down. Continuing the pull for longer times will eventually lead to some flow in the sample, so that its length will continue to increase very slowly as long as I keep pulling on it.

When I release the film, part of its return to its original length will take place quickly, as in a rubber, and still more recovery of the sample will take place more and more slowly. But any increase in length resulting from what we have called flow can never be undone, for we have not applied the push necessary to make the material flow back in the other direction.

What is the explanation of these three different kinds of viscoelastic behavior that blend almost into one? They all arise from the motion of segments of the polymer chains past one another, in roughly the following sorts of ways. Materials that show all three kinds of response are usually polymers that have rather strong intermolecular forces (which we talked about in Chapters 1 and 4), so that they tend to stick together. (But they must not be crosslinked, or they could not flow.) The points at which the molecules are stuck together by these intermolecular forces act somewhat like crosslinks, so that the polymer responds like a rubber when we begin to pull it. That is, there is some uncoiling and unkinking of the chain segments between the stick points as they take up more extended conformations, just as we described earlier.

But the intermolecular stick points are not strong and permanent, like the crosslinks in a rubber. As the pull continues, they begin to break apart, letting longer segments of the chain uncoil a bit, only to form again and slow down the stretching process. These rearrangements take more time, so we see the stretching going on gradually in what we call viscoelasticity.

Finally, since there are no real crosslinks, the molecules begin to slide past one another, a segment at a time, and this we call flow.

When we stop pulling, the restoring force of the chains trying to regain their less-extended conformations makes the process reverse, first rapidly as the short segments between intermolecular stick points coil up, then more slowly as the breaking and reforming of the stick points help this process. But where whole molecules have slid past one another, these changes will remain because there is no force that tends to make them slide back again. The sample is permanently changed, and we say that flow has occurred.

As we have already seen, not all polymers show all three kinds of viscoelastic behavior. In rubbers, the intermolecular forces are chosen to be low, and flow is prevented by the presence of crosslinks, so that all we see is the first, or truly elastic, part. In other polymers, if the temperature is high enough and there are no crosslinks, there is usually so much flow that we don't see the earlier parts of the viscoelastic response at all. And there can be other variations, too, all depending on the particular kind of polymer present.

The viscoelastic film I described at the beginning of this section is used as the inside layer of the glass-plastic-glass "sandwich" that makes up the "safety glass" used in this country in automobile windshields. If there is an accident, and the glass is broken (all too often, unfortunately, by someone's head), the gradual stretching of the tough plastic film tends to bring the object being forced through the windshield to a stop with a minimum of further damage.

You may have seen another material showing visco-elastic response, the gumlike stuff called "Silly Putty," which doesn't seem to have much use except as a toy.

When you throw it on the floor, it bounces like a rubber ball, because only the elastic response is rapid enough to take place so quickly. Try to hold it in your fingers, however, and you will find that it flows enough to drip slowly away.

THE GLASSY STATE

We have now described several ways in which polymer chains can move about in bulk materials (that is, with no solvent or other small molecules present). In each case we have said that the temperature must be high enough for these molecular motions to take place.

Now let's think about the other case, in which the temperature is not high enough, and we can expect something else to happen. What then?

Then, there is no longer enough heat energy available to allow the groups of atoms making up segments of the polymer chain to move about. The atoms must stay close to whatever positions they were in when the temperature was lowered. Molecular motions of the sort we have described cannot take place. This is a common situation in another sort of material you are all familiar with: glass. We describe polymers in this state of limited or "frozen" molecular motion as glasses, or glassy polymers, too.

Rather surprisingly, the change of a polymer from the molten or rubbery state to the glassy state as the temperature is lowered, or back again as it is raised, takes place over a very short range of temperatures. The temperature at which the change or transition from the rubbery to the glassy state takes place is called the *glass-transition temperature* for that polymer. Just about every polymer has one. It may be far below, near, or well above room temperature, depending on the chemical nature of the polymer.

What sorts of changes take place at the glass transition temperature? Above it, the polymer may be rubbery or viscoelastic, or may show only a tendency for very slow flow. Below it, all molecular motion of segments of the chains stops. The polymer shows the properties we associate with glass: It is hard, stiff, and rather brittle—easily broken by a sharp blow. If—as we have assumed up to now—it is amorphous, it is likely to be clear and transparent, as is most glass also.

Some widely used polymers are below their glass-transition temperatures in normal use. One group, called the acrylics, is utilized whenever the best clarity and transparency is needed. It is used for the clear glasslike canopies of aircraft, for tail lights, instrument covers, and decorations on automobiles, and in similar applications. It is stronger and tougher than glass (though not nearly as strong as the crystalline plastics described in the next chapter), and is not affected by long exposure to sunlight and rain. Other members of the acrylic family, you recall, are used as automotive lacquer films because of their excellent resistance to outdoor exposure; these polymers are, however, tailored to be hard and tough rather than glassy and brittle in thin-film form.

Another material, polystyrene, looks quite like the acrylics but is less resistant to weather and somewhat more brittle. It is also less expensive, and finds wide use for small molded articles such as toys, models, and hundreds of others for which long life and the best strength are not essential.

Chapter 10

THE PROPERTIES OF
CRYSTALLINE POLYMERS

In this final chapter of our exploration of the nature of giant molecules, we shall complete our survey of those properties of polymers that make them useful to man by considering what I believe to be the most fascinating of these marvelous materials, the tough, strong crystalline plastics that I—and many others—like to call "engineering" materials. In this group fall plastics that can replace metal pieces of the same size with great savings in both weight and cost, and the synthetic fibers that have so revolutionized our dress and our homes.

To understand the structure of these crystalline polymers, and to see the relations between this structure and the desirable properties of the materials I have mentioned, we must explore one more group of methods for looking at atoms and molecules. But this time we do not wish to investigate the properties of giant molecules, one at a time, when they are dissolved. Rather, we must start by studying the orderly arrangements of short sections of polymer chains in the solid material, and then see how these ordered regions—crystals—fit together to produce larger and larger structures that ultimately determine the properties of crystalline polymers.

X-RAYS, ELECTRON BEAMS, AND POLYMERS

As a student many years ago, I can remember Peter J. W. Debye pointing out the wonderful coincidence of

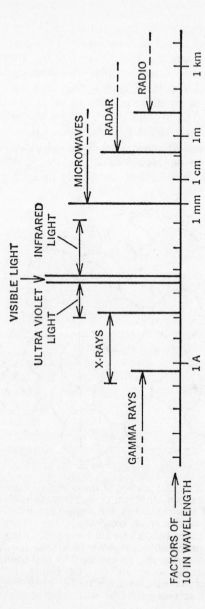

Fig. 52. The electromagnetic spectrum.

nature that gives visible light just the right wavelength to
study the sizes of polymer molecules. (We described this
technique in Chapter 6.) Now we want to explore something a thousand times smaller: the distances between
atoms in a solid material (a few Angstrom units) rather
than the size of an entire polymer chain (a few thousand
Angstroms). Can we find the right kind of "light" to do
this?

The light that we see is a small part of a family known
as electromagnetic radiation; as Figure 52 shows, we
know different members of this family by such names as

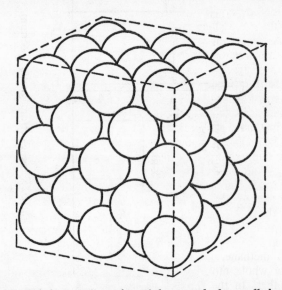

Fig. 53. This is a small portion of the crystal of a small simple
molecule like oxygen, nitrogen, or methane. In each case, the
molecule itself is not spherical, but it spins around and around
in the crystal, so that if we could see it, the molecule would
appear like a fuzzy ball. These balls are packed together just
as you might pack marbles together in a box. The X-ray experiment tells us what this arrangement is, and how far apart
the centers of the molecules are. Of course, in the real
material, the crystal extends much farther in all three dimensions than I have shown.

X-rays, ultraviolet or infrared light, and radio waves. A quick look at the figure provides our answer: The wavelength of X-rays is in just the right range for studying intermolecular distances. Professor Debye knew this well, of course, versatile physicist that he was. In fact, he had developed the use of X-ray scattering for this purpose thirty years before he became interested in light scattering by polymer solutions.

The results now of interest to us come from a somewhat different sort of interaction between X-rays and crystalline materials, called *diffraction*. At this point I will not describe the experiments of X-ray diffraction, or how results are obtained, but merely tell you what some of the results are as they apply to polymers.

As we might expect, X-ray scattering experiments give us information on the sizes of small molecules. But X-ray diffraction experiments give more detailed and more useful information about the arrangement of the atoms in crystalline substances. They tell us, for example, that molecules like those of the oxygen or nitrogen in air, or of methane, act as if they were little spheres or marbles packed closely together when they are frozen (at *very* low temperatures) to their solid crystalline form (Figure 53). And they tell us that in common table salt (sodium chloride), atoms of sodium and chlorine are arranged in alternating fashion, first one kind and then the other, in the three-dimensional structure suggested by Figure 54.

But let us not fail to notice a distinct difference between these two crystal structures. For some small molecules like methane, the X-ray diffraction experiments tell us how whole molecules are arranged with respect to one another. In the salt crystal we can't even find anything that looks like a molecule containing one atom each of sodium and chlorine, although this is what beginning chemistry students are always taught is the structure of table salt. The crystal structure suggests that a "molecule" of salt is as big as the whole crystal—the grain of salt that comes out of the salt shaker on your dinner table.

Well, these are different kinds of substances from the polymers we have been studying, and this is not the place to explore their structures further. The point to be made is that we have to be careful about interpreting the results of X-ray diffraction experiments on polymers, particularly when we try to decide what a molecule is or what molecular weight the polymer has. It is simply not possible to answer these questions from the X-ray experiments alone. In the early days of polymer science, when there were still arguments about their really having high molecular weights, attempts to do so led to great confusion.

What the X-ray diffraction experiment tells us in the case of a polymer molecule is, first, the arrangement of

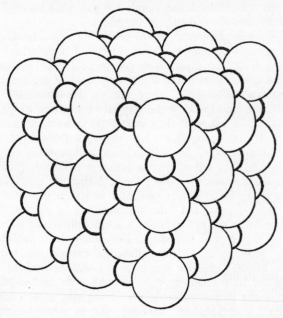

Fig. 54. This figure shows a por... of the crystal of common table salt, sodium chloride. Here we see sodium and chlorine atoms packed closely together in alternate fashion. They do not pair off to form separate molecules of NaCl; in fact, if we ask what size the "molecule" is, we have to say that it is as big as the whole crystal. Again, only a very small part of that crystal has been drawn.

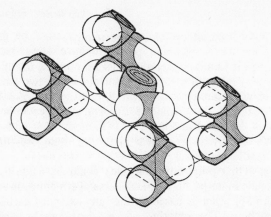

Fig. 55. In the crystal structure of polyethylene, we see how the polymer chain runs through many successive unit cells, so that any one unit cell contains only small parts of several neighboring polymer molecules. Failure to understand this confused the early polymer physicists, used to thinking in terms of structures like that of methane shown in Figure 53. They could not see how a very large molecule like a polymer could fit into a small and simple unit cell. (Adapted from my *Textbook of Polymer Science,* second edition, Wiley-Interscience, 1971.)

the atoms in a short repeating section of the polymer chain; and second, the arrangement of neighboring chains with respect to one another. Let us again use as an example the plastic with a very simple repeating unit, polyethylene, whose structure we saw in Chapter 1 was a series of $-CH_2-$ groups joined together. The crystal structure of polyethylene as sketched in Figure 55 shows us that the carbon-carbon bonds of each polyethylene chain are arranged in the fully stretched zigzag conformation we saw earlier in Figure 3.* X-ray diffraction also shows us the way in which neighboring polyethylene chains lie alongside one another, as shown in Figure 55.

* Actually, the X-ray experiment does not show the positions of the hydrogens directly, since they are too light to diffract X-rays strongly. We can infer their positions from knowledge of the C-H bond length and the angles between the bonds of the carbon atom, as discussed in Chapters 1 and 2. Figure 55 was drawn with this knowledge in mind.

The crystal structures of a large number—at least fifty to one hundred—crystalline polymers have been determined, and it would not serve any useful purpose for us to look at very many of them. I want to show you two more, however, which are typical of two different groups of polymer structures. These are the *isotactic* and *syndiotactic* structures described in Chapter 2. (I suggest that you review this chapter to get a clear picture of these structures before reading further.)

We saw that poly(vinyl chloride) could be made as a syndiotactic material. It, too, has a crystal structure, shown in Figure 56, which is based on the fully extended carbon-carbon chain. The chlorine atoms, considerably larger than the hydrogens that would be in the same positions in polyethylene, stick out on each side of the carbon-carbon chain, as shown in the figure. Neighboring

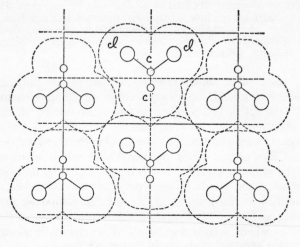

Fig. 56. The crystal structure of poly(vinyl chloride) is typical of those of many syndiotactic polymers. Here we look at the polymer chain end-on, seeing the positions of successive carbon atoms and the larger chlorines coming off first to one side, then the other. The hydrogens are not seen. (Adapted from my *Textbook of Polymer Science*, Wiley-Interscience, 1962.)

chains are pushed apart a little bit to make room for the chlorines, but the structure is very similar to that of polyethylene.

In an isotactic polymer, of which polypropylene is a typical example, the situation is a bit different. There is not room enough, in polypropylene, for the $-CH_3$ (methyl) groups, on every other carbon atom but on the *same* side of the carbon-carbon chain, to be accommodated when the chain is arranged in the planar zigzag conformation. Something has to give, and since (as we saw in Chapter 4) rotation around carbon-carbon bonds occurs relatively easily, the polymer chain in polypropylene is pushed out of the fully stretched zigzag arrangement into the regular spiral conformation shown in Figure 57, in which the methyl groups stick out away from the backbone without interference from other atoms. This

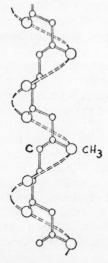

Fig. 57. Many isotactic polymers, such as polypropylene (shown here), have crystal structures based on a spiral arrangement (dotted line) of the carbon-carbon backbone. (This and Figures 58 and 60 are adapted from my *Textbook of Polymer Science,* second edition, Wiley-Interscience, 1971.)

type of structure, with a spiral backbone, is found in many polymer crystals including most isotactic polymers and many biological materials such as proteins.

When the substituted groups, like the chlorines or methyls we have been discussing, lie randomly on alternate sides of the chain, we have an atactic polymer. In those cases where the substituents are fairly large—as are those mentioned—the polymer cannot be made to crystallize. It may be a glass or a rubber, as we discussed in Chapter 9, but it cannot be made into one of the engineering plastics that are the subject of this chapter.

So far, we have explored only the interaction of X-rays with polymers. But it is well known that, just as light has some properties of waves and some of particles, so do electrons. And when electrons have the right energy, as they do when they are pushed by a high voltage, they have wavelengths of about one Angstrom. Thus, a beam of high-voltage electrons is another tool with which to explore arrangements of atoms and molecules.

Just as we can form magnified images of small objects with a microscope, operating with visible light, so an electron beam can be made to form images of even smaller things, in an *electron microscope*. The laws of optics show that the smallest objects we can see with either kind of a microscope are about the size of the wavelength involved. Thus, with visible light we fail to see even the biggest polymer molecules, while with the electron microscope we can almost—but not quite—see single atoms. This ought to make the electron microscope a good device for looking at polymer crystals, in which many atoms of the polymer chains are arranged regularly. Indeed, this is so, and the exploration of the structure of crystalline polymers with the electron microscope has led to excitingly unexpected results, which we shall discuss in the next section.

THE MORPHOLOGY OF POLYMER CRYSTALS

It is now time to consider the arrangements of the crystalline regions of polymers in solid plastics and fibers, and to see how these arrangements give the properties of strength and toughness to these materials. These arrangements make up what we call the *morphology* (the word means form) of crystalline polymers.

The interaction of X-rays with polymers gives more information than the crystal structures described in the previous section. First, the X-ray diffraction patterns characteristic of crystalline polymers are always accompanied by some scattering of X-rays, indicating the presence of amorphous material. By looking at the relative amounts of these two kinds of results, polymer physicists decided that crystalline polymers were never entirely crystalline; only part of their atoms were in crystals. They calculated degrees of crystallinity ranging from about 40 per cent to 90 per cent in typical cases.

Second, the experiments gave clues to the size of the crystallites. Typically, these were estimated to be no larger than a few hundred Angstroms long. This is, of course, shorter than the length of the polymer chains themselves. So, it was concluded, a polymer chain must go through or be a part of more than one crystalline region. The picture of a partly crystalline polymer that fitted these observations showed, as in Figure 58, small crystallites

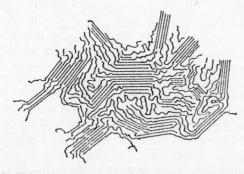

Fig. 58. This sketch shows the crystalline-amorphous nature of the fringed-micelle model of a crystalline polymer, considered to be correct for many years but now largely abandoned.

(called micelles) surrounded by amorphous material. The polymer chains were thought to pass through several micelles and their edges or fringes, and to be tangled up in the amorphous regions in between. This was the fringed-micelle model, and it was accepted as correct for over twenty-five years.

Then, about fifteen years ago, the electron microscopists began to examine polymers in earnest. Almost simultaneously several groups of them made the fascinating discovery that it was possible to produce single-polymer crystals by cooling a dilute solution of the polymer—much of the early work was done with polyethylene—and that these crystals were more like those of low-molecular-weight substances than anything seen before in the polymer world. The form of these crystals was often a thin diamond-shaped platelet, called a *lamella* (meaning a thin sheet), like that shown in Plate 12. The size of such a single crystal was typically several tens of thousands of Angstroms across but only about one hundred Angstroms thick, about the ratio of width to thickness in the sheets of paper on which this book is printed.

Moreover, electron-diffraction experiments—just like X-ray diffraction but done right in the electron microscope —showed without any possibility of doubt that the polymer chains ran in the direction of the *thickness,* not the width, of the lamellae. Here was a dilemma indeed: How could a polymer chain many thousands of Angstroms long pass through a crystal, in a direction in which it was only a hundred Angstrom thick, without an awful lot of amorphous material to hold the rest of it? There were, as Plate 12 shows, no amorphous regions to be seen anywhere.

There was only one answer: The polymer chains had to be folded back and forth, as depicted in the model of Plate 13. This answer has proved to be correct, as far as we can tell, and has been accepted by most polymer scientists today. Single crystals of many different polymers have been studied in the past ten years, almost all of them showing the characteristic folded-chain structure.

Needless to say, it was not long before the polymer physicists began to examine solid bulk polymers with the

electron microscope. And at once they found lamellae—
everywhere. As indicated in Plate 14, the entire volume
of a highly crystalline polymer seemed to be filled with
lamellae, larger and less regular than those in single
crystals but still showing the characteristic thickness of
around one hundred Angstroms and requiring a folded-
chain structure.

Since there were again no amorphous regions to be
seen, and the lamellae were much larger than polymer
crystallites had been thought to be, it was clear that the
fringed-micelle theory had to be abandoned. An alterna-
tive interpretation of the X-ray data had to be found. We
now think that the scattering once attributed to amorphous
regions arises from the presence of defects in the polymer
crystals. By this I mean atoms or groups of atoms that are
not exactly in their normal places in the crystal structure.
Possibly they arise from some minor chemical difference,
such as a head-to-head monomer of the sort described in
Chapter 2. Several other kinds of defects have been
observed.

Thus, our present picture of the structure of solid polymers is based on a rather imperfect folded-chain lamella
as the building block. Further studies with the electron
microscope and the light microscope show that these
lamellae are parts of still larger structures called *spherulites* (Plates 15 and 16). These are roughly spherical in
shape, and can grow to be as large as a few hundredths
of an inch in diameter. We do not fully understand why
they grow as the photographs indicate.

In fact, there are many things we do not yet know
about the structure of crystalline polymers. We realize, for
example, that the lamellae must be bonded together at
many points in order to account for the strength of these
materials. Probably these bonds result from a polymer
chain passing through two lamellae every once in a while,
as the sketch of Figure 59 suggests. There appear to be
other structures beside the lamellae that are important
in some cases, too. This is an area of extremely active
research, and it is possible that this picture of the morphology of polymer crystals will have been modified consider-

ably between the time that I write this sentence and the
time that you read it.

PLASTICS AND FIBERS
AS ENGINEERING MATERIALS

Except in the farthest corners of the earth, it would be
hard to find anyone alive today who is not aware of the
tremendous advances in the world of science and engineering that recent years have brought. Man has created
wonderful machines and structures, and it has taken many
different sorts of knowledge to make them possible.
Among these, I want particularly to call your attention
to new materials.

The materials of which things are made fall roughly
into three groups: metals, ceramics (including glass), and
polymers. In the last century scientists and engineers have

Fig. 59. We think, although we do not know with certainty,
that lamellae are held together by some polymer chains that
run through two or more lamellae instead of folding in a
regular fashion.

learned how to produce materials in each of these classes that are new and different from anything that existed before. Often, these new materials have been made as the result of research to produce a substance with particular desirable properties, such as great strength, toughness, transparency, or something else required for a new product of engineering skill. It is appropriate to call such new things *engineering materials*.

Crystalline polymers are engineering materials, and as such are becoming more important all the time. I would like to close this book by telling you a little about them: first, engineering plastics; then, composite materials, in which plastics are combined with other materials such as glass; then, finally, fibers and other forms of plastics in which strength in one or more directions is increased by a process called orientation.

Before the polymer scientist learned how to make and use his materials to best advantage, the word plastic came to suggest a cheap substitute. In the years I have been associated with the field I have, thank goodness, seen this concept largely disappear. Indeed, there was a time when it was justified, and we still see—all too often—cases where the wrong plastic was chosen, or a plastic was used where it should not have been, with unsatisfactory results. But today a plastic is far more than a substitute for something better (and many of them aren't cheap, either). More and more we find a plastic used where nothing else will do the job, or used to do a good job where another material was unsatisfactory.

What do plastics have to offer? On what bases do they compete with and replace other materials? Often they have unique properties that cannot be equaled in any other material. For example, the best electrical insulators in existence are plastics. As I mentioned at the beginning of this book, things we take for granted today, like television and radar, could not exist until synthetic polymers were developed. And of course we saw in Chapter 9 that all rubbers must be high polymers. So are practically all glues and adhesives.

Then, plastics often compete because they are light in

weight. A four-inch cube of steel weighs about twenty pounds; a similar cube of polyethylene, only two. Of course, a piece of polyethylene is not nearly as strong as a piece of steel of the same size. (Polyethylene is not the strongest engineering plastic, either.) But some plastics are stronger than metal pieces having the same *weight*.

Finally, plastics can compete with other materials in price. That is, they can often do the same job, or even a better one, for less money. One reason why this may be true lies in the ease with which complicated shapes can be produced in plastics. The processes of molding and extrusion, described briefly in Chapter 9, allow extremely complex forms to be produced quickly and automatically, whereas to produce the same object in another material might require much costly hand work.

Given these advantages, it is not surprising that plastics are taking their place alongside of, and no longer as poor substitutes for, other materials.

Among the outstanding engineering plastics are polyethylene and polypropylene, the nylons, and polyoxymethylene, whose chain structure has the repeating unit $-CH_2O-$. All are highly crystalline. I shall give you only one or two examples of their uses as engineering materials, in addition to those we have mentioned from time to time.

Both nylon and polyoxymethylene are tough materials that withstand repeated blows or pressures very well. They are useful for gears in relatively light-load applications, for example in adding machines and automobile speedometers, where they have gone far to replace metals. Another property that contributes to their success in this use is the fact that they never have to be lubricated. This property of nylon is used in many other applications in the automobile, in which many parts last their lifetime without the frequent lubrication required only a few years ago.

When properly molded, polypropylene has the ability to undergo flexing vast numbers of times without failure— a one-piece hinge, so to speak. I have a polypropylene key case with a molded "hinge" between the two halves that I have opened and closed many times every day for over six years. It looks a bit shabby, but the hinge shows no signs of failure. Many automobiles use similar hinges on the accelerator pedal.

Polyethylene and polyoxymethylene, as well as some other plastics including poly(vinyl chloride), are finding increasing use to replace metal in pipes of all sizes. Their resistance to corrosion is particularly important here.

The family of engineering plastics is not limited to these highly crystalline materials. There is another group of structures in which the role of the crystallites in producing strength and toughness is taken by different materials. These structures—and I use the word to indicate something put together—are called *composite* materials. One of them, undoubtedly familiar to you, is the family of glass fiber-filled plastics widely used to make fishing rods, archery bows, pole vaulters' poles, and other tough, springy devices on the one hand, and large, strong pieces such as boats and sportscar bodies on the other.

Now glass is potentially a very, very strong material, but its surface is easily attacked by moisture and traces of other chemicals to produce microscopic cracks that make it brittle. By coating glass, in fiber form, with a flexible plastic, these cracks can be covered over so that they no longer lead to failure of the glass. The composite material has much greater strength and toughness than either glass or the plastic alone.

Other composites consist of tiny particles of rubber embedded in and chemically bonded to a flexible plastic. These composite materials resist impact better than any other substances known.

But we still have not mentioned the strongest and stiffest polymeric materials of all. They are the synthetic fibers (and certain related plastics), the nylons, acrylics, and polyesters so popular for wearing apparel of all kinds. How absurd, you say; I can break a nylon thread easily. Yes, but consider how tiny it is: in reality, it is stronger and stiffer than a steel fiber of the same size.

This great strength results from a further modification of the structure of crystalline plastics. This change is called *orientation,* and it is carried out by a stretching process called *drawing*. During the drawing process, the things that get oriented, or moved into a single direction, are the polymer chains. Somehow, they all end up running in the direction of the fiber itself. I say somehow, because we do not yet know much about the details of the process. But let's see how it works.

In Chapter 9 we mentioned briefly that a synthetic fiber is made by a modification of the process of extrusion called spinning. Molten polymer is pushed through an

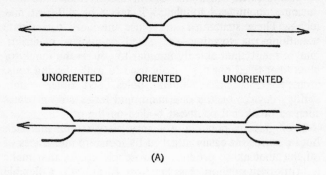

UNORIENTED   ORIENTED   UNORIENTED

(A)

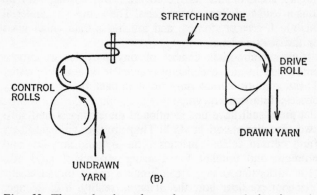

(B)

Fig. 60. These sketches show the process of drawing. At (A) we see a magnified view of a single fiber at the point where "necking down" occurs, as explained in the text. The apparatus used to produce drawing is sketched at (B). Plate 17 shows the "necking down" in an actual fiber.

array of tiny holes in a metal plate called a spinneret. It comes out into the air in long, spaghettilike strands but much thinner. As the strands cool, they solidify, crystallizing in the lamellar structure, and are wound up on a bobbin. Later, they are unwound and stretched.

During the stretching or drawing process, something unusual happens. The polymer strand suddenly changes in diameter, getting smaller and longer, as depicted in Figure 60 and Plate 17. We say that it has "necked down" to perhaps half its original diameter, and at the same time become about four times as long as it was before. This change is accompanied, as you can imagine, by drastic alterations in the morphology of the polymer. Lamellae may be destroyed and reformed, or may just slip past one another and change the directions in which they lie—we don't know, in detail, which happens. Spherulites, originally roughly spherical, end up more nearly football-shaped, with considerably fuzzier outlines than before. Most important of all, X-ray diffraction experiments show that most of the chains tend to run nearly in the direction of the fiber axis.

This preferred orientation of the chains leads to much higher strength along the fiber axis, and correspondingly less at right angles to it (where the loss doesn't count in a fiber). Other properties improve also, and what was a moderately good material before orientation becomes a strong, tough synthetic fiber so useful to our present-day living.

Orientation can be made to take place in larger plastic pieces, but with correspondingly greater difficulty. In a flat piece such as a film or strip of material, orientation in two directions, one along and one across the piece, can be produced as the result of a "two-way stretch." Again, strength and toughness are remarkably improved. Here is a final example:

The next time you see a large packing box or crate encircled with the familiar black steel strapping, about half an inch wide and a sixteenth-inch thick, take a closer look: You may be seeing a piece of doubly oriented plastic. The same width and thickness as the steel, even the same color, it looks just like the metal it replaces. But it does an even better job, duplicating the steel's strength while providing elasticity that lets it keep a snug grip during a bounce or jar that would snap the metal in half. Amazing? Not really, just typical of the application of a plastic as an engineering material.

And so we come to the end of my story. But not the end of the story of synthetic polymers, for I am confident that man has just begun to understand, tailor-make, and put to use for his own great benefit the molecular nature of synthetic high polymers.

REFERENCES

If this story of synthetic polymers has been of interest, you may wish to read further. Unfortunately, most books written in this field are at the college level or beyond, but here are a few that will not tax your understanding too much:

Big Molecules by Sir Harry Melville (Macmillan, 1958) is a small book that you will find very easy to read. Several paperbacks, in order of increasing difficulty of subject matter, are: *Giant Molecules* by Morris Kaufman (Doubleday Science Series, 1968); *Plastics for Engineers* by G. R. Palin (Pergamon Press, 1967); and *The Nature and Chemistry of High Polymers* by Kenneth F. O'Driscoll (Reinhold, 1964). Still more advanced, but probably still useful to you with judicious skipping of some material, is my own *Textbook of Polymer Science,* second edition (Wiley-Interscience, 1971).

A beautifully illustrated book showing what we think molecules, large and small, may look like is *The Architecture of Molecules* by Linus Pauling and Roger Hayward (Freeman, 1964).

Finally, the *Life* Magazine Science Library published in 1966 *Giant Molecules,* by Herman F. Mark and the Editors of *Life,* a lavishly illustrated book giving an overview of polymers that makes good reading for the whole family.

INDEX